D1633661

The Memoirs of a Crafty Dog

Found: a Penny

The Memoirs of a Crafty Dog

My journey

from abandoned racer

to media star

CHRIS DIGNAM

Found a Penny

Crafty Dog Books Cymru,

Ti Levran,

59 Capel Road, Clydach,

Swansea, UK. SA6 5PY

www.crafty-dog-cymru.co.uk

Copyright © 2019 Chris Dignam

Photographs/Illustrations by the Author

Copyright © 2019 Chris Dignam

(Except P184, top, © Nan Horgan Photography)

ISBN: 978-0-9576932-4-1

DEDICATION

This book is dedicated to those other great greyhounds
that have made our lives richer for their humorous and
often inspiring stories; notable amongst these are Mr Barry
Clarke, Mr Arthur Carr and, though not a Greyhound, an
honorary one, Mr Bosley Boodle Clark.

Also to Penny's Nana and my own Mam who would have
loved this book.

FOUND A PENNY

ACKNOWLEDGEMENTS

Penny and I would like to thank Pam Dormer and Rachel Moakes for being thorough and careful editors, and Nan Horgan for the use of her photo on P 184.

Penny would also like to thank Jan, Andrea and the team at Animal Doctor's, Clydach for all their support

FOUND A PENNY

CONTENTS

FOREWORD

Sally had been our first greyhound. A fabulous companion, clumsy and intelligent, loyal and loving on what was for us - and for her - a steep learning curve. Using this new-found hard-earned knowledge, Sally was followed by a couple of foster dogs who had been damaged in different ways and were in need of fixing. Then by the gentle and sensitive Sammy. Their stories are told in my first book, 'A Hound in the House'. We felt that we were prepared for the next foster - who turned out to be as amusing and amazing as the others and maybe even a little bit more!

Rather than write about our view of life with our greyhound, this book is written from her viewpoint. It's the story of an abandoned hound who learns about living in a home with a family and all the adventures that come with it. Importantly, it is what she makes of the strange people, places and things she encounters along the way and what she gets out of it - all seen through the eyes of the greyhound herself.

This is her own story, which began on the day we found a Penny.

DEFINITION

Greyhound - A dog of a tall, slender breed having keen sight and capable of high speed, used since ancient times for hunting small game and now chiefly in racing and coursing.

Origin - from Old English grīghund; the first element, related to Old Norse grey 'bitch', is of unknown origin.

Crafty - Involving or relating to the making of objects by hand; Clever at achieving one's aims by indirect or shrewd methods.

.

FOUND A PENNY

INTRODUCTION

THE PENNY BLACK

That time when we were without a dog was a strange one. It was nice in some ways; we could come and go as we pleased, make our craft items, leave paint and brushes, or jam jars and fruit everywhere, could have lie-ins when we wanted. Being able to eat all of a meal and not having to leave a bit. In short it allowed us to be totally selfish. On the other hand it could be not so nice. Coming home to an empty house for example, lacking any sort of family routine, even that loose one we used to have. The worst of all was the lack of someone to nurture.

After our fosters we were still a bit wary - maybe even a little bruised. We had self doubts that we would ever find the right dog again. Sally and Sam had been so very magical and the others, though special, had been broken in various degrees. How we ended up with our next rescued greyhound was a bit of a coincidence.

I returned to work after being on leave to find an e-mail from a colleague in another section of the council. He had found a lurcher wandering on the beach in Port Talbot and with some others wanted to get it caught safely and looked after. The local pound would take the dog but there was always the fear that if not claimed the dog would be put down. Rich (my colleague) contacted me as he had heard that I had links with Greyhound Rescue Wales. So, I contacted Sarah at the rescue kennels and discussed how to get the dog captured and then rehomed.

Before we could put any plan into action, Rich called to see me and told me that the lady who had first seen the lurcher had managed to feed him, get a lead on him and take him home. After considering taking him to the rescue kennels she decided that he fitted in so well in her family that she would keep him.

I e-mailed Sarah to let her know that the great plan wouldn't be required. Sarah's reply was to ask us whether Armelle and I wanted to do some fostering again, and that she had a few dogs in; they were three black greyhounds, notoriously difficult to rehome as they weren't considered to be as pretty as the other colours. One had been brought in by a trainer, one arrived from Ireland and the other handed in by a farmer. They were all around 3-4 years old. She told us to have a think – there was no pressure.

We mulled things over for a while but we'd taken our holidays and most of the craft fairs were over for the summer too, so it might be a good time to give another dog a go. Even if for a month or so, it would be a nice distraction. I contacted Sarah and let her know we could pop over on the Friday afternoon as I was off work so we could see the prospective fosters.

We chatted with Sarah and she said that she thought one of the dogs would be a better fit than the others; she had been abandoned and was wandering in a field in Mid Wales where she had been taken in by the Farmer who found her. He looked after her for a few days until Greyhound Rescue collected her and so she ended up with Sarah. Armelle and I were open to whatever she thought was best so Sarah disappeared and came back with a tall black greyhound on a blue lead. Her coat was rough but with a slight shine, she was so thin but her eyes were bright and had that certain sparkle. They didn't know the dog's name and hadn't had time to research the numbers tattooed in her ears - all we knew was that as she had numbers in both ears she was an Irish girl. She was very affectionate and came over immediately for a cuddle from both Armelle and myself. Sarah brought out her small terrier which the new dog took very little notice of. Again, this was a good sign of her being small-dog friendly. We walked the dog around the paddock where she came with us confidently and with a brightness which belied the fact we had never met before. She really seemed to love people. When we got back to the courtyard I explained that we had the last couple of seasonal craft shows so couldn't collect her until the following weekend. Sarah agreed but said that if we weren't keen, if someone else wanted her, then could she go with them? I looked down into the greyhound's deep brown eyes and she stared trustingly back. That unmistakeable connection was made between us – "No," I said, "keep her for us; we'll give her a chance."

Armelle and I were quite excited as we drove home, thinking about what we needed to get for her and when would be best to collect her. Sarah had called the dog Susie; a name that we thought really didn't suit her.

I suggested Poppy, but a black poppy? That wasn't right. Armelle chimed up with "What about Penny – like the Penny Black stamp?" So, we might not have had the dog yet, but we had a name. Penny.

This is her story – in Penny's own words

FOUND A PENNY

PROLOGUE

MY EARLY LIFE

I am a greyhound, born in Ireland, a land over the sea from where I live now. From as far back as I can remember, I used to run. As soon as my eyes opened properly, I ran around with my brothers and sisters and I can remember my mother catching me and gently lifting me to put me back in the bed with the others. It was a continual game of escape and then capture, but always done ever so gently, as she didn't want to hurt us.

As soon as I was strong enough, I was taken away and put in a pen with other dogs that, despite all their different colours and sizes, were all the same as me. The human that looked after us called us "greyhounds" though it also called us lots of other names, many of which I later found out weren't kind ones. Every few days more young dogs joined us, and others left,

1

collected by other humans. We never knew where they went. My actual brothers and sisters, who I'd known from the days with my mother, got fewer and fewer, until there was just me and my sister. She was black like me but with more white on her feet, but she didn't have the white chest and chin that I have. We tried to keep together over the weeks as we grew taller, our noses pointier and our bodies longer and slimmer. We slept against each other, trying to stop the other dogs pushing in between us as they scrabbled to get space on the shredded paper that was spread across the floor of the cage we all shared, and I suppose called "home". All the dogs smelled strange to me, apart from my sister who still had that lingering scent of our mum and our family.

Early one morning as we both huddled together (it must have been winter as it was very cold, and the water in the drinking bowls had gone hard so we could only lick at it, and when we did that it hurt our tongues) a man (we had learned to tell the difference between man and woman humans) came over to our pen. He was talking to the human who looked after us and pointing at some of us. They were talking very loud which made me feel uncomfortable - maybe even frightened - and the man's finger pointed at me. I froze, as a pair of arms leaned over the edge of the pen and made to grab me around my middle. I wanted to pull way from him, but there was just no room and nowhere to go; all I did was bump into other pups. I felt myself being pulled up into the air. I looked down at my sister and saw her face as, distraught, we realised that this would be the last time we would see each other. I remember trying to call out to her, but the man put his hand over my snout, and I was carried as a bundle out of the shed into the daylight.

I was put in the back of what I later found out was called the "van". There were two other dogs from my pen, neither of whom I knew very well. The van was dark and smelled of wee and wet paper and I will admit I was so frightened that I also did a wee too. It was a very worrying time for the three of us. The door was shut and there was a loud rumble as the van rattled and shook. It felt as if it was moving though we didn't know where.

That was how I got to the man who was called my trainer. There were six of us, three from my pen and three from another van-load and we were brought together in a large cage which they called a crate. It also smelled of wee and other dogs – lots of them. The six of us were given names but we gave ourselves our own names. I can't remember what the human called me, but to my new family I was Blackie. There was a white dog with a black nose and spotty face called Smudge, a fawn boy called Ginger, a fawn girl called Dear (she often said "Oh dear" to herself), a large white and black dog we called Basher, because he kept bumping into things, and finally a black dog we called Shiny, because he had a shiny coat and sparkly eyes. We all got on well, and in a few weeks we accepted that we were a family. That was the thing with being a greyhound – you learned to adapt and accept whatever came to you.

The man who fed us (I don't want to say "looked after" us as there was precious little actual looking after carried out) watched as we grew bigger and faster and picked out those of us who could get to the front of the chasing pack of hounds. That was when I saw my first racing track. It might have been a bit tatty and the kennels there were dirty but to us greyhounds, it was all very new and exciting. There were twelve of us in the back of the van; standing on wobbly legs, bumping against one another, looking out of the open back doors as a group of men looked in, arguing, shouting and jostling as they pointed back at us. One by one, we were lifted out of the back and stood on the paving where the men stood in a tight circle around us. They made me walk around and roughly tugged at my ears and checked my teeth. I was bundled into another van with three of my fellow exhibits, the door was slammed shut and in the darkness we were carried off on a long journey.

The van stopped once and a man in a peaked hat and blue jacket looked in and checked us over. The door closed again and we were driven up a small slope. There was a lot of noise of vans and cars outside, revving engines and shouting. After a while it went quiet, apart from a rumbling sound – the van lurched, and we felt ourselves moving. It was a strange feeling, not just forward but also up and down and sideways. Two of my travelling friends were sick as they didn't like the feeling at all. I too wasn't very happy about it, but I wasn't actually ill.

We tried to sleep but the movement was so unpleasant; as we lay down we slid across the boot of the van, bumping into one another. After what seemed an absolute age, there was noise, shouting, banging and clanking, the van engine started and we moved off.

We did have sight of daylight after a few hours,

though it was only brief. Most of us had been unable to hold for the length of the journey and I am ashamed to say I was one of the ones who weed on the shredded paper on the floor of the van.   At least that was all I did, unlike a few of the others. You can't imagine how much that van stank by the time we got to the end of our journey. It was dark when we got wherever that was, so we went from a dark van into the dim light of torches and a few street lights, into a set of new kennels.

This was where we were trained to race. Our trainer was quite nice to us and we soon learned that the more times we got to the finishing line first then the better we were treated. I was quick and I got to the front more often than most of the others. I met my "owner" and his wife on a few occasions at the training track and they were also quite nice to me. They "owned" a few of my racing friends as well, so we were a sort of family, albeit a strange one. Black, brindle, fawn, blue and white. A real mixture!

We used to go in a van (this time one that didn't stink of pee and poo) in crates - two of us to a crate - to the real racing track. It was huge, brightly lit and smelled of people. It was so noisy too, with announcements, dogs barking, people shouting or just lots of people talking loudly. I remember being pushed into the racing trap for the first time and I thought that I would never be able to race out of it as it was so incredibly loud outside. Fortunately, the excitement of the other dogs was so contagious that I found myself being wound up by it and joining in the barking. As soon as the gate clanged open, I was off out of the trap and up that track as fast as my legs and body would let me go. I exploded from the gate, flinging grass and sand up in my wake, fighting to be the quickest of us, to get to that metal hare. I was the first one past the line – it was incredible how happy the people were, including my owners who appeared from out of the crowd. They stood me on a table and had their photo taken with me (I found out about photos and cameras a lot later). Then they disappeared into the crowd and, winner or not, I was put back in the van with my friends and taken back to the trainer's kennels.

This went on for a few years but as I grew older I noticed that I wasn't always first, or even second. Some newer dogs had come to the trainer. They were becoming more popular than me, as they got to the front before me on more and more occasions. I also started to notice that after a race, some of the dogs who had come with us weren't in the van going back to our kennels. I just knew that as the old dogs changed over, I was going to be one of those that didn't go back. We had all spoken amongst ourselves as to what happened to those dogs, but we never knew. Someone mentioned being rescued as he had heard people talking about it but another spoke about something to do with a meeting with a large bolt, but I didn't know what that meant – it just didn't sound very good.

After one race, my "owner" appeared. He took me on my lead out into the large car park, which by this time was emptying quite quickly. He handed some money to a nice man who walked me to his own van. "Want to go for a drive, boy?" he asked. I did try and tell him I wasn't a boy, but by then I'd been lifted into the back, the door slammed shut and we were driving off.

That was the end of my glittering racing career.

1 - ALONE

The door of the van squealed open and I peeped warily out. We weren't in the city; there were no buildings that I could make out, there was only a wide sea of long grass.

"Out you come boy, time for a walk," the man said. He pulled a rope lead over my head and I jumped out onto the ground; it was soft and more than a little wet and my feet sank into mud. The door slammed shut behind me as the man pulled me away on the lead. It dug into my neck because I wasn't quick enough and a bit unsure about what was going on. I liked a walk as much as the next greyhound but there was something here that didn't feel quite right. I started walking, picking up the pace as he started to walk faster. The air was damp in the big field and I was picking up the smell of many strange things on the breeze. When I stopped to scent the air the man slipped my lead over my head and off. I was free.

"Go on then - have a run," he prodded me. I looked at him and then stepped forward. I started to walk, then trot and then I ran. It was fabulous to have that freedom to just run, to stretch out and fly across that field over the mud and grass, kicking bits into the air as I went. As I approached the far end of the field I began to turn and was going to head back in the direction I'd come from. I stopped; they weren't there. The man and the van were gone.

I didn't know what to do – I just stood there, all alone in the huge, empty field, panting from the exertion of running, just watching and waiting. He would be back any minute, I told myself. I slowly retraced my steps to where the van had left me. The gate it had driven through was shut and it was too tight for me to go through. I did manage to push my long pointy nose through the gate to see down the lane and I thought that I might have just caught sight of a van turning in the distance at its very end. He must have had to go somewhere but obviously he would come back for me.

I waited. It was damp, and the air grew chillier

– I could feel the cold climbing up my legs. I missed my old jacket; it might well have seen twenty greyhounds before me but for the time that I had it, it had been mine. I told myself that he'd be back soon.

I waited. Birds began to gather in the hedge and trees along the side of the field near the gate. Huge black ones with long, sharp-looking beaks and straggly wings cawed at me. Some were braver and came down to sit on the top of the gate to stare down at me. Their cold black eyes, sparkling like ice, made me feel even more uncomfortable. I stepped slowly and cautiously away from the gate and made my way along the edge of the field. There had to be another gate, or maybe a hole in the hedge somewhere. When I walked many of the black birds followed me, hopping from bush to bush, all the while keeping up their constant screeching.

Still I waited. I was getting colder, the air was getting wetter and for the first time I began to feel scared and started to have doubts; what if the man had forgotten me? What if when he came back he couldn't find me – it struck me that being a black dog in a field that was getting dark he might not be able to see me.

I could see one distinct clump of trees taller than

11

the rest alongside a pile of stones up against the hedge; it looked like it had once been a building. I continued towards it. The tumble of stones was still a shelter of sorts and I hoped that it would keep some of the rain off me – the icy rain that had now started to fall in huge freezing cold drops the size of my paws. I huddled tight against one of the walls to be out of the draught as the evening sky grew darker and darker. I'd prayed that the man would come back to collect me, but it was now that I started to accept that he was never going to come for me. I was on my own.

The rain beat on the rusty iron sheet over my head; it rattled and cracked as the drops hit it and slid down to land with a slap in the invisible puddles of muddy water that were all around me. I stood there all night, desperately tired but too scared to even shut my eyes. At one point I could no longer hold my eyelids open and I must have fallen asleep. I was woken by a pain in my left back leg and I barked and kicked out - something scurried away into the dark. I never slept after that and I was so relieved to see the fingers of light pushing over the distant hedge as the sun finally came up after what had seemed like a year. When I looked down to my leg I could see that something had bitten me and left the marks of their teeth in my fur. It had bled but this had now stopped.

My stomach gurgled. When had I eaten last? It must have been the bowl of water and vegetables that I'd had before I'd left the kennels. Looking around the ruined building I could make out what must have been old food stalls for animals. I pushed my nose in and rooted through to find any traces of food but anything that had been there was now long gone. There were only spider's webs, mud and rust. The field was growing lighter as the sun had cleared the distant hedge. I moved carefully out into the open, back towards where I thought the gate had been but there wasn't a gate there. Somehow the night had confused my sense of direction. I went further out to the middle of the field. It was vast. I could see a metal shape on legs – it was worth a look as it might have food in it. Luckily for me it did; dried bits of food which were obviously not for dogs, but I didn't care - it was food after all. It tasted musty and the cake was stale. I shuddered to think how long it had been there, though the water in the bin next to the food was fresh, probably due to the heavy rain. It was better than nothing. Carefully, I went all round the edge of the field looking for a way out; I found two gates, one of which was the one out onto the lane. I knew I couldn't get through that one. The other gate led into another smaller field. Was there just enough room on one side between the edge of the gate and the stone pillar it was tied to for a greyhound to try to push through? No. The gap was too small. I sighed and made my way back to the other gate where I stood for a while, hoping someone would pass. Nothing. I turned and made my way back to the shelter. And waited.

This became my daily routine. I'm not sure how long for as the days merged, interspersed with black, fearful nights. Try and sleep with an eye open, then to the bin for a scrap of animal food and water, watch the gate, then back to the shelter. I found a patch of old straw at the back of the shed that smelled of another strange beast – again, I didn't dare to think what it was. At least the straw was dry. It helped me to conserve a little bit of body-heat in the dark evenings and overnight.

One time I heard a van in the lane. I managed to get up and even tried to run to the gate but I wasn't quick enough. I almost laughed – I'd been quick enough all my racing life but this was now my story; the greyhound that wasn't fast any more. I was growing weaker as the small handful of dried animal food and water wasn't enough to sustain me. I went back to the gateway into the small field and tried to squash myself through as I'd done for many days now without any luck. I must have been growing thinner because this time I managed, with a wriggle, to squeeze through.

It was yet another field but at least it was a different one. I trod slowly round the edge, keeping close to the hedgeline for two reasons; to look for a way out, but also in case anything unfriendly in that field wasn't too pleased to see me. The grass here was cropped shorter and there was a scent of animals that was much fresher than in the other field. The first field had seemed to have been as abandoned as me, but someone or something had been in this one recently. The green dropped away in front of me as I reached the top of a slope. This led down towards another hedge and gate – and beyond it, a group of buildings, noise and movement! I was excited, but now I was also wary. I went down the hill keeping the hedge to my left, moving slower as I was cautious but also because I had very little strength left to move any faster. I could hear a human voice the other side of the hedge, though further away. I halted and pushed myself into the rough grass and sticks at the foot of the hedge to hide. I was so weak I couldn't keep my eyes open - I drifted into a fitful sleep with dreams full of giant mice with blazing red eyes and huge, sharp teeth.

2 - MR JONES

I woke with a start when I felt a nudge in my face from a cold, wet nose. I was too tired to even be terrified as I looked up into a pair of the strangest doggy eyes I think I have ever seen; they were bright blue and ever so slightly cross-eyed. "Hello, and who are you?" came the voice. It was distinctly doggy, but with a very strong accent.

"Blackie," I replied. My voice was dry and cracked.

"You're in a pretty sorry state," the black and white boss-eyed dog told me. "You don't look as if you have been chasing my sheep. You don't look able to chase anything!"

"I'll have you know that I am a champion racer," I answered trying to raise my head and look noble but failing miserably.

"Oh really?" the collie smiled. "You stay here –
I'm going to get you some help." Off he went, leaving
me lying beneath the hedge.

Within a few minutes he had returned, barking
over his shoulder towards a human who was coming
with him. He was a short, round man in a long muddy
raincoat with equally muddy rubber boots. "Well, well,
what do we have here boy?" he asked his dog. He
walked with a stick that I noticed was carved with a
dog's face on – a black and white collie-dog like my
rescuer.

"A champion racer, she told me," the collie
replied. "But she's very weak. Been abandoned by the
looks of it," the dog continued.

"A racing greyhound. Been abandoned, I think.
My, she looks very weak," the man spoke, bending
toward me.

The collie tutted, "I know- that's what I just
said!"

Though he had a coarse, weather-beaten face

that had seen many hot summers and wet winters, his eyes were soft and kind and as he looked down at me I could see them getting a little watery. "My poor girl, what have they done to you?" He brushed my brow with a firm but caring hand that made me reach my head up.

"Twm, you stay with her – I'm going to get the Landrover." The man stood up and walked away. Twm the collie lay by my side and snuggled up to me; for the first time in weeks I felt that something good was going to happen to me at last. "Don't worry, Blackie. We'll look after you. You'll be ok – Mr Jones will make sure of that."

In what seemed like an age but was probably only a few minutes, a mud-streaked Landrover pulled up and Mr Jones stepped out. He opened the back and after leaning down and carefully wrapping a sheet around me, lifted me and set me down in it. He tenderly pulled the old blanket round me and told me that he would get me home and I'd be safe and sound at last. He said this in a human language I didn't recognise, but I could understand what he meant. Twm the collie jumped in beside me and guarded me all the way to the farmhouse where Mr Jones lifted me out and carried me into his kitchen. It was wonderfully warm and had a magical smell, which I discovered from Twm, was wood smoke from the open fire and freshly baked bread. A lady came over to where I was placed in a heap of old blankets near the fire. She too had seen many summers and winters like Mr Jones, and had a mop of grey hair and glasses, through which another pair of kindly eyes looked at me. "Poor girl." She spoke in the same strange language (which I later learnt was Welsh). In her hands she bore a small bowl of something warm and welcoming – a thin soup of meat and vegetables. It wasn't too hot and to my hungry mouth was the best thing I'd ever eaten.

"Slow down, girl," she chided me, "You must be so empty. Only a little now, and a little later. Little and often as my Mamgu used to say,"

Twm was still close by, watching over me. "I told you they'd look after you." As I slept (so Twm told me afterwards) Mr and Mrs Jones talked about me. How could people be so cruel to have dumped me? Where was I from? What should they do? They fed me little bowls of soup all that day and into the next, until I was strong enough to sit up and eat my own bowl. I met the rest of Twm's family too – three other very boisterous working border collies who were very eager to greet me. It was all a bit much and Twm had to step in and ask them to give me a little peace. It was so nice resting by the warmth of the fire surrounded by the sheepdogs. It reminded me of when I'd been a pup amongst my brothers and sisters all those years ago. There was something particularly comforting in having other dogs lying alongside you, listening to them snoring - though the occasional breaking of wind and a growl of "Pardon me" wasn't quite so welcome!

A few days later, after a very nice breakfast and a walk round the garden with Twm, I jumped up into the Landrover and Mr Jones drove us out of the farmyard and down the road. I moved closer to Mr Jones to listen to him as he told me what the next turn in the adventure of my life would be. Mrs Jones had been in town a few months before and had met some people from Greyhound Rescue, who told her all about what happened to many ex-racing greyhounds. When she had put some money in their collection pot one of them gave her a leaflet which had details on all about the work they did. That was why she had been so upset when they had found me. Mrs Jones had rung the number on the leaflet and they had offered to come up and collect me as it was such a long way for the farmer and his wife to travel. Mrs Jones had insisted that they wanted to take me to the rescue kennels as she wanted to see me safe, but they had eventually compromised and we met the lady from greyhound rescue half way, in the car park of a pub. Mr Jones shook the lady's hand, they spoke a while and then the lady slipped a collar and lead over my head. As I stood in the back ready to climb down she stroked my head and gently lifted my ears. They had always done that at the race track but there they were never that gentle. I knew she was reading the numbers that were written there. The lady looked so kind and I could smell dogs on her – better than that, I could smell greyhounds!

I stood in the back of the lady's car, watching Mr Jones walk towards the Landrover and turn to see us drive away. I smiled and barked once as he waved me goodbye. I was sad to leave him, but I will never forget Mr and Mrs Jones and how they saved me from that cold wet field and got me back on my four paws again. In their language, "Diolch yn fawr".

The lady (who told me her name was Sarah) talked to me as we wound our way through the roads then narrower lanes towards the kennels, where she said, there were many other greyhounds like me. She had already collected two more black dogs the day before, and in all she had 14 dogs at the rescue centre. Three were going out in the next day or so, but just as fast as dogs went out, there were always more coming in.

3 - THE RESCUE KENNELS

The kennels were behind and below a house where there was also a paddock and exercise area. Sarah's husband came out to meet us, and together they walked me round the house to the kennels at the back. I was greeted by a sea of very excited and curious greyhound faces, all eager to introduce themselves. The pen at the end had a small greyhound girl in it and it was here that I was taken to. Sarah made a note of the ear tattoo details, gave me a bowl of food (which I was very grateful for, I can tell you!) and then went off to sort out the other dogs. As I ate, the little greyhound approached me, ever so quietly. She was older than me, a pretty little brown brindle girl who introduced herself as Hazel. As soon as I finished my food we greeted each other properly with sniffs and nudges. She was a bit shy, but to be honest so was I, as I'd had such a whirlwind day that it was all a bit much. Hazel lay on her bed next to mine and explained to me about life here and what was likely to happen.

Hazel had been a traveller's dog and she had hunted rabbits at night with a bright light they called a lamp (they had the lamp, not her – I'd made the same mistaken assumption too, which she had found highly amusing!) until she became lame. They had left her tied to a hedge where, fortunately, someone had found her and handed her in. She had seen the vet and her leg was now much better after warmth and rest. Some people had come to see her and she was hoping that within a few weeks, she might have what her and the other dogs called a "Forever Home". The family had little humans (they called them "children") which she was looking forward to playing with and protecting. I told her about the Jones's who had rescued me. I only briefly mentioned the race track. Hazel said that she thought I would get a home soon too. I hoped so – a home like the Jones's, with wood smoke and fresh bread with butter on it.

I met most of the other hounds at the rescue kennels over the next few days. They were a real mix of many colours, ages and backgrounds. Some were from over the sea in Ireland like me, most were ex-racers. One, a black boy called George, I recognised and when we talked he told me he had raced at Swindon where I had raced too. He had been handed in a few months back and was going to a foster family the next day. I asked him what that was. George explained that though each of us would spend some time in the house with Sarah and her family, it was much better if we could go to a real house with real people and spend some time with a proper family full-time. These people could then find out what we needed, what sort of home, whether we were good with children or animals. But before we could go to live with a family we all had to see the vet and have an operation. I asked him what sort of operation and he winced and looked down between his back legs.

"Oh," I said.

"Quite," he replied. "But to have a forever home with a family it's worth the sacrifice. I think it is. Well....I hope it is!" He beamed back at me and wagged his huge tail.

Hazel went the next day with another three dogs – three greyhounds and one shaggy lurcher – in the van to see the vet. She came back in the early evening, very groggy and very sore. Sarah laid her next to me on her bed and promised to come in and check her throughout the night. Hazel was talking in her sleep and trying to wriggle but when she did, it made her wince with pain. I had a look at her; her lower tummy was bald as it had been shaved and up the middle was a red line with black zig-zags. I recognised these from the track – stitches holding a wound together. I could only guess at what that operation was all about and I didn't like what I was guessing. It made me shiver. I watched over Hazel all evening as she moaned and whimpered in pain. Sarah came in every hour to check her and she took her temperature and carefully checked the wound wasn't bleeding. At one stage Hazel was sick - I had to bark to call Sarah, who was two kennels away, and she came running in. She fetched a bowl of warm water and a cloth and wiped Hazel's mouth and face and took away the towel she was lying on to replace it with a fresh, clean one.

By the morning Hazel was sleeping better, and by late morning she was awake and able to get up for a little food. Sarah and her husband kept coming round to check the dogs who had been to the vet. Three had had this operation and another had just had a check over and their claws trimmed. That was Ronnie, a very highly strung brindle hound, who was convinced that his claws had also been a major operation and that he should have tablets for the pain too! All the while I kept thinking about the dogs at the track who had gone to see the vet but we had never seen again. That made me shiver.

Within a few days Hazel was up and about and able to exercise gently in the paddock, and I went out with her too. She was a lovely little greyhound and I was both sad and pleased when the human family came to see her and chose her for their own. I saw the family – two big people and two "children" who were all absolutely smitten with Hazel as soon as they saw her. She put on a real show, on her very best behaviour, quiet and gentle and very affectionate. To be honest, that's what Hazel was like all the time. They were definitely going to home her, and would be back the following week to collect her. Hazel left the kennel the next day and spent the week in the house with Sarah and her family so she had some practice at being in a human home. We did have a couple of exercise sessions in the paddock together, where we could catch up on news. She told me that she had heard Sarah saying that I was going for my operation in the next batch – which made me worry, though Hazel told me there wasn't anything to worry about.

The afternoon before my operation, Sarah took me up to the house and once again she checked my ear tattoos and then took my photo. "We'll put you on the webpage next week," she told me. "Is that ok, Suzie?" I looked round to see who Suzie was and realised that must be what she was calling me. OK, for a home and family, I was happy to be called Suzie. "You're off to the vet tomorrow. As soon as you're back, we'll put you on the web." I'd no idea what she meant – I knew a web was something spiders made and I'd seen betting slips and pages, though how spiders and betting books came together was just beyond me!

Hazel's departure that evening left me feeling sad; we did have time for a kiss and a snuggle and I wished her the very best of luck. "Don't worry," she told me. "I know that black dogs are difficult to rehome, but I'm sure you won't be here long."

I was shocked. "What? What do you mean?" I asked her.

Hazel frowned. "People think that you black dogs are not pretty enough so are reluctant to take a black dog home." She saw my face fall. "But Blackie....er Suzie, I'm sure that won't happen to you. You're so pretty and happy and bouncy." I was more than a little concerned by what Hazel had said, but I did my best to push it to the back of my mind.

Another four of us were loaded into the van the next morning and went off to the vet. Jim and Mick were brothers (white and fawn hounds, though one had a smooth coat and the other a shaggier coat), and Jessie was a big, loud lady lurcher. A lurcher is apparently a dog who has one parent a greyhound and the other a different breed of dog. They often look exactly like any other greyhound, but in Jessie's case her Dad had been a bull terrier so she was stocky and had a squarish head. The journey was bumpy though thankfully not a long one. We were unloaded quite efficiently and taken to the crates at the back of the building, where we were checked over and prepared ready for surgery. The boys went through first and came back barely awake.

I went down next; a lovely young lady took me through to the "theatre" (I think that's what she called it) where they lifted me onto a metal table and then put a needle in my leg. I fought to keep my eyes open and even tried to get off the cold steel table, but it was no good – I drifted into a sleep of dreams about people with large knives and scissors.

I woke up in the crate in the vets with the two boys in the crate next to me. They were looking at each other, surprised and annoyed at the fact that their "boy bits" had gone missing. Jessie was in the crate the other side of me and she was still sleeping soundly. My belly was sore, and I was too frightened to look at what they might have done to me. I fell back to sleep. When I woke next, I was back in my own bed and Sarah was leaning over me, stroking my face very gently.

"How are you feeling, Suzie?" she asked me.

I tried to answer, but my throat was so dry. Sarah had a wet cloth and wiped round my mouth, which helped to wet my lips and tongue. My belly was sore and I winced when I moved. "I'll bring you a painkiller," she told me. "You rest and I'll see you in a while."

I woke later and Sarah was beside me again. I

could see past her that it was still dark outside. She wet my lips and mouth again and slipped a small tablet into my mouth, which I swallowed and drifted back to sleep.

It was light when I next opened my eyes and stood up gingerly. My head felt as if my eyes were spinning in circles and so was the rest of the world but that was all going the other way. It made me feel sick but I was determined to go out to the front of the kennel to see the others. The brothers had been put in the one next to me and they were both up, standing and swaying a little in the run at the front of their kennel. They were pleased to see me and we greeted each other at the wire.

"Any sign of Jessie?" I asked.

They both shook their heads (slowly as it made them feel dizzy). I began to worry but then I heard from the run further up the kennels, "She's ok. A bit groggy but she's been out to have a bark at the world then gone back in to rest." It was Ronnie the namby-pamby lurcher who called to us. The three of us breathed a sigh of relief to hear that she was ok.

Over the next few weeks we exercised a bit more each day and after a fortnight Sarah felt that we were back up to health. Jessie and the boys even managed a gentle run together in the paddock. I went along and tried to join in, but when I stretched my legs out my belly stung sharply where the stitches had been, so I pulled up (stopped running). Jessie trotted over to me and very loudly announced, "Come on girl – you're not going to get better unless you push through the pain barrier."

I looked down to the floor, "But it hurts,"

"Mind over matter, my girl!" the lurcher barked at me.

I began to trot, but as soon as I stretched out it twinged again. I know it might have made me look soft, but I was frightened and I didn't care what bossy Jessie might think. I slinked quietly back to my kennel only to find that I had a new companion! She was another black greyhound girl called Spot. She was all black apart from one white patch in the middle of her face that looked like a blob of paint. It was my turn to tell her about everything that went on here; the daily routine, forever homes, foster homes, little human pups called children. I winced as I sat down and Spot tilted her head inquisitively.

"I've had an operation at the vets." I told her.

"What sort of operation?" came the question.

"I'm not really sure but it's the girlie version of the boys losing their dangly bits."

That was as good an explanation as I could give. Anyway, what was Spot's story?

She said that she was only two years old and had been raised in the Midlands. Her breeder wanted to race her at Perry Barr track, but when he trialled her she wasn't very fast. So, he had offered her to one of the rescue groups and after a few weeks with one group she had been passed on to Sarah's.

As we were speaking I heard the door to my run being opened; it was Sarah with lead in hand. "Come on Suzie, there are some people who want to see you."

I was really excited as she told me that two people she knew were looking for a foster dog. They were interested in seeing me and two of the other black dogs, as they knew that we were the most difficult to home. She also said that they were used to greyhounds, had had two of their own and had fostered a few as well.

Be on your best behaviour, I told myself, remember what Hazel had said to me - don't blow it.

Sarah took me up the steps and around past the kitchen to the large flat area at the side of the house where she had taken my picture; here they were sitting at the table and chairs and looking expectantly at me.

"Here's the first one of the three black dogs. She was found in a farmer's field in Mid-Wales. He was a nice chap – they phoned me and she was handed in."

"Why do they abandon them in a field?" the man asked.

"The farmer will see them as a wandering dog and shoot it to protect his livestock. It gets thrown in the hedge and no-one is any the wiser," Sarah answered.

"That's awful," he said, shaking his head.

I walked up to the man; he wasn't very tall, had a round face and glasses and smiled a lot. He stroked me and looked into my eyes – gentle eyes, I thought. I then moved over to the lady; she was very pretty and had sunglasses on, which she took off to look at me. I liked them as they seemed very kind and happy - I brushed against both of them in turn and Sarah handed the man my lead. I was soon being walked round the garden by the man and the lady, and they passed the lead from one to the other to see how well I walked with them. Like Hazel had told me, I was on my very, very best behaviour. As we walked, they were talking about me and saying how beautiful I was, how calm I was, and other lovely things like that. I was hoping so much that they would like me and want me. I was wishing and praying from the depths of my heart - to be honest, I never heard everything they said. I just wanted safety and security. A home and a family to belong to at last.

When we walked back to the table and chairs, Sarah brought over her little terrier, to see how I would behave with small dogs. "Don't worry....I'll be good," Jack the terrier said, as he winked at me then walked past. I knew he had a habit of biting your ankles if you weren't looking but, in fairness, he too was on his best behaviour!

"So what do you think?" asked Sarah.

"We've got a couple of fairs coming up so can't pick her up for a few weekends." The man said.

"We are really busy, but we'd love to take her," the lady added.

"OK," Sarah spoke, "So if anyone comes in the meantime, would it be ok for Suzie to go with them instead?"

The man thought for a second, looked deep into my eyes then replied, "No, keep her for us – we'll give her a chance."

I watched them walk away, ecstatic that I'd been offered a foster place, but also sad that I had to wait again for it.

Back in my kennel I couldn't wait to tell Spot what had happened, about the lovely people and that they liked me and would be taking me home soon. Spot was as pleased as I was, and we spent the rest of the evening talking and imagining what their home was like, if they had human pups, if they had a garden with lots of trees, or a paddock. Did they have a huge kitchen (with a smoky wood fire) full of baking bread and cakes like Mr and Mrs Jones? Would they feed me lovely things? I slept well that night and dreamt of living in a doggy palace, being waited on by my new humans, being fed the finest food and sleeping on a huge soft bed.

The next two weeks dragged slowly by, each day seeming to last a week. We dogs may not have a great sense of time, but in this case it was almost slowing to a stop. Every day, as soon as I heard people moving up at the house, I would rush to the front of the kennel only for Sarah to pass me by. Then one morning Sarah opened the kennel to put a slip lead on me and took me up the steps to the house. "Time you got a bit of house practice young Suzie," she told me. "You'll be going in a few days and it would be good for you to see how a home works."

She opened the door and I went into a room that smelled of cooked food. There were two dog beds in there alongside a row of wooden panels, one of which she pulled and it opened like a door. Inside it was a bag of dog treats (along with many other rather uninteresting things). Sarah handed me a stick chew – the first time I ever saw one. I took it off her, mumbled a "Thank you" and walked around the room with it in my mouth. I sat in one of the beds (well, no-one else was using it) and held it in my mouth. I wasn't sure what this chew was for, but one thing I did know was that it was mine. After a few minutes I felt myself beginning to dribble so I swallowed – and discovered that it tasted of the chew and that it was nice. I bit into it – and then realised what it was. From that point I didn't need any more prompting!

Over the next few days I learnt that Sarah and her family went in and out of this room (they called it a kitchen not a "gegin" as the Jones's had) all day. When they ate in here, I would walk over and try to put my head up to see what they were eating - it all smelled wonderful. They didn't tell me it was wrong to put my head up, but I soon learnt that if I sat in my bed I got treats, but if I hung round the "table" (another word I picked up) I got nothing. At night I slept in here with that grumpy terrier of hers. We got on alright really; I just needed to keep away from his food bowl. And his bed. And his special blanket. Apart from those, he was fairly easy-going!

I did get to see the rest of the house but to be honest, the kitchen was the room that fascinated me most. I think that was mainly because I was always hungry. I was in the kitchen licking my food bowl to remove any last traces of dinner when Sarah came in to call me. She picked up some papers off the table and slipped a lead over my head. "It's time, Suzie. Or should I say Penny." I looked at her with my best puzzled face. Who the heck was Penny?

Sitting at the table and chairs outside were the man and woman who I'd seen those weeks ago; it hadn't been a dream, they had come back for me at last. I was so excited I felt like I was going to burst. I rushed over to them and rubbed myself against them, they stroked me and ruffled my ears. I sort of heard them speaking to Sarah, but I was so happy that only part of it went in. I think they said that I was to be a foster, but if everything worked out, then their home could be my home. Inside I told myself that it had better be a good home or else I would come back here. I liked this kitchen!

I kissed Sarah goodbye and the man (who was called Chris) and the lady (who was Armelle) walked me to their car. The back door was open and Chris beckoned for me to jump in. I looked up at the car, and then to the man. I was still so unsure about stretching that I wouldn't risk the twinge of pain if I tried to leap up. I just stood there and hoped that he would understand. It worked – he knelt and, wrapping his arms around my legs, lifted me up and placed me in the back of the car. It had a thick blanket and a dog bed in. They pulled the back door down, started the car and off we went. I stood and looked back at Sarah's rescue kennels and watched it disappear as we turned out of the drive onto the lane. Nice as it had been, like Mr Jones's farmhouse, I hoped that I would never have to stay there again and that I'd now found my forever family..

"Suzie" on the GRW site – before I became Penny

Below – when I came home – still room for a few more good meals

4 - FOREVER?

I stood up most of the way through the narrow winding lanes trying very hard not to fall over (though I have to admit I was pretty wobbly). When we got onto the wide fast road I lay down, as I guessed that we would be going a long way on this one. At one stage the car stopped, so I got up, as I thought that we we'd arrived – the car moved off again and I fell over; this balancing in the car lark was going to require a fair amount of practice. I stood up at the next stop and well, if it wasn't another bendy bit so I wobbled round again! A few minutes later, when the car stopped once more, I wasn't being fooled, so I stayed down. Only when I heard the engine go quiet and movement and talking from the front did I think that it was now safe to assume we were at the journey's end. OK then – what was home (foster or not) looking like?

I peered through the rear window of the car at my prospective home and could see that it was a big house (or so I thought, until I learned later that these were three houses joined together) with a nice front garden and a super big van parked next to the grass. I remember my trainer had one of these in which he used to take his horse or a few dogs in crates. I shivered a bit at the thought of that. Chris put a nice new (at least to me, though I could smell that another couple of dogs had worn it before) red collar on me and clipped on a lead. "Come on then, Penny," he said to me. All I thought was "Again that name Penny! What's wrong with Blackie?" I shook my head – "right, suck it up and get on with it. What's the problem with another new name?"

I stood and waited until Chris lifted me down. Armelle told him that he would soon get bored of that! They walked me up the drive to the front door (which had a picture of a black greyhound on it!) and Armelle opened it and went inside and Chris invited me to follow. In front was a high hill of steps covered in carpet that led to who knows where? But we didn't go that way. Instead we went through a door into a long room; my nose could just pick up the scent of dog in there, a few dogs, but two were very strong. I spotted a lovely bed next to a chair (I knew about those from Mr Jones and Sarah's houses), but before I could even give them a sniff, I was hoicked on my lead through to the kitchen (looked nice) past some food bowls (empty) into a small grass area. Here he unclipped the lead - I was so glad of this as I really needed a wee. If Chris had looked closely, he'd have seen a huge smile on my face as I let out a ginormous lake. When I finished, I turned to go inside but Chris presented me with a biscuit. Ah – wee here means a treat. I made a mental note of that. I'd always been taught by my Mum that you never messed in your bed or in your home so evidently this wasn't classed as inside the home.

As we had come through the kitchen, I'd clocked a bed out of the corner of my eye, close to the food bowls. Excellent choice of position, Chris! Armelle was at the other end of the kitchen filling the kettle with water. (I think I should add here that I didn't know what many of these new things were called until later, but rather than sound an idiot I have used their proper names from the beginning). Chris got a bottle from the cupboard – milk – and took it to over to the kettle. As he brought it back to the cupboard he stopped and asked me whether I liked milk. I just licked my lips. So, he poured some into "my" food bowl. I lapped that up! That was when I decided that I loved him and would follow him to the end of the earth - or at least around the kitchen and back.

So that's what I did all the rest of that day; wherever Chris went I was close behind, which worked well until he went up the mountain of steps to the top of the house. I stopped and just watched him go up and disappear around the corner. The first time I just stood and waited for him to come back down as I could hear him talking to me from upstairs. I cried the second time he went up, and even put my foot on the first two steps, but I just wasn't brave enough to go any further The third time I thought – "blow it, I'm going," and I ran as fast as I could, throwing myself up the stairs with my legs paddling like mad. I got to the top and was astonished; I'd discovered greyhound heaven! In one room was a huge bed. I could tell from the scent that it was Chris and Armelle's bed. It was quite tall and I couldn't get on it, as I was still too reluctant to jump. At the end of the long corridor was another room with just as big a bed which didn't smell of anyone. I guessed that this must be mine! However, this was also too high up, so I reasoned that until I was better (if that ever happened) I would have to sleep downstairs. By the food bowls.

Armelle had come up the stairs now too; she called Chris who came out of the bathroom and stood beside me. They spoke together as I just stood there, wagging my tail, looking from one to the other and smiling as broadly as I could.

"Penny," Chris said to me. I looked up. "You need to come downstairs with us. Do you understand? Is that ok?"

I smiled. I'll be honest, I didn't really understand what he was saying which was true of most human conversations, but I got the gist. I knew it meant going down the scary stairs but that they would be there to help me. Chris put his hand through my collar, gently moved me to the top step and tried to move me forward. There was no chance – I froze. There must have been a hundred steps in front of me – the hall was miles and miles below. He was very patient; he knelt in front of me and put my chest against his shoulder. Armelle stood beside me and held my collar. Step by step Chris moved my feet and Armelle held me steady, as we made

47

our way slowly down to the bottom. When we got to the last three steps Chris let me go and I jumped the rest, nearly lifting my backside over my shoulders. Phew! I wasn't going to go up there again! Ever!

I slept on my dog bed next to Chris's chair whilst they watched the tellybox. I couldn't see the interest myself. Later that evening they had a little food, gave me a small meal and let me out in the garden for 'last wees' (that was a familiar routine that Sarah had started with us dogs). I came in, climbed into my kitchen bed and curled up. Chris sat at the table for a while, reading. He spoke to me for a few minutes until I fell fast asleep. I opened my eyes once in the night – Chris was gone, but I was too tired and comfortable to go and look for him. From the next room I could see a light shining, which meant that I was not in the dark and I felt safe. I knew from that moment that this was going to be my forever home, and that they were to be my very own Dad and Mam. I sighed and wriggled into my blankets.

I awoke on that first morning with a feeling of real excitement mixed with an over-generous helping of apprehension. The sun had been up for a while – I could remember dreaming a little, though nothing of any sense remained with me; it was all pictures and noises. The car – the old van – Mr and Mrs Jones – Chris and Armelle – dinner last night. As I started to rouse myself properly, I could hear the sounds of movement upstairs and then, of someone coming through the room next to mine – curtains being pulled open and blinds being turned. The kitchen door opened and my new Dad came in, smiling. "Hello Penny", he said, kneeling beside my bed. I stood, stretched noisily, smiled back and leaned forward for him to rub my head. It was so different to have a welcome like this. He got up and crossed the kitchen, opening cupboards and the big white thing by my bed, which I found out was called a "fridge". He took my food bowl over to the other side of the kitchen (I followed - practically clamped to his side) and then brought it back and set it down. In it was milk and what he called "crunchy nut flakes". I sniffed them, licked at them – they were nice – and then I emptied the bowl. I stood by the table as Dad ate his own breakfast and I tried to get my head up on the table-top but he told me "No", in a firm, though not unkind, way. I sat back in my bed, and as soon as I did, a small piece of cooked bread with fruit jam on it came my way. It was lovely –

sweet but crunchy too. I could taste butter on the bread – I love butter! I got up again but nothing came over to me. As soon as I sat back in my bed more food came to me. OK – another lesson learned – sit in my bed when they eat and I get some bits of his food. Fair enough!

After his breakfast, Dad clipped my lead on and we went out into my new street, past the white van and the car. We walked past houses and lots of other cars too. All the smells and the images were overwhelming – there was so much to see and so many strange scents from people and lots of other dogs. Down the road we went and around a corner where we came to a large field. Here it smelled so much of dogs but I couldn't see any at all. As soon as I stepped on the grass I had to wee and poo as I was absolutely bursting! I sniffed the air and, with Dad by my side, we set off together across the field. There was a building over to my left, and then this huge, flat grassed area. As we walked I began to feel nervous; why are we in this field? Where are we going? I slowed down as a thought crossed my mind – was I going to be allowed off for a run and then turn to find myself alone again? I stopped walking and stood stock-still; if I didn't move, he couldn't leave me. All the time Dad was still talking softly to me. We stood together for a little while, then turned back the way we came and with his encouragement I went with him and we retraced our steps back to my new home.

I relaxed as we got closer to the house and I almost ran up the drive to the door with the greyhound on it. By the time I got back to the kitchen, Mam was there too, and I made sure that I showed her how much I loved being here, in my new home. There was no way that they weren't going to realise how much I cherished this place and being with them. I followed Dad round the house again all day, stopping at the foot of the stairs as they were still daunting – well, coming down at least.

Mid-day Mam and Dad had a meal and I had some scraps with a little dried dog food and water. I was beginning to realise that food was a regular thing here - and often too! The afternoon passed quickly after a long nap and another shorter walk. Before I knew it, it was my tea-time. This, Dad told me, was my "main meal of the day". They had eaten their own meals (which I'd watched intently). Once or twice I'd stood and gone over to them as they ate but they both said "No" and told me to wait. So, it was now my turn to eat. Dad carried my bowl into the room they called the "Utility Room".

This was where my food was kept in a huge tin in a cupboard high up on the wall. (Mental note - I would never reach this without a really long run and jump!) He carefully measured out some dried food and took it (with me following closely) into the kitchen where Mam scraped the remains of their own dinner into my food bowl with my dried food. There was also some of their meal still in the cooking pot and this was added too, and water. My mouth was watering as I could smell this food and I was shaking with excitement in anticipation of what it would be. Dad brought the dish over and put it on the raised stand on which my bowls rested.

I stopped for a few seconds just to survey what this was; it was twirly red stuff in a sauce which had cheese on it (I'd been given cheese by Mr Jones so recognised it). I looked up at Dad.

"Your first Italian meal, Penny. It's Fusilli pasta twists in a Bolognese sauce with a little Grana Padano cheese grated on top. Enjoy!"

It was fantastic. You can't imagine how acute a dog's senses are and how sensitive their taste buds can be – and for the first time mine were in overdrive; all my nerves were firing; tender meat, rich tangy sweet sauce and crunchy kibble. I later found out that the sauce was made with tomatoes and basil that they grew themselves. The meat was beef, which they bought in the local village. It was indescribable how wonderful all of this was to me – a dog that had lived on sloppy veg. soup at the track was now dining on food fit for a Queen! I was amazed that anyone would go to such trouble to make a meal like this for me.

After my meal, we went into the room with the tellybox, and I had a sleep whilst they watched it. When I awoke, they had changed their clothes and Dad had my lead in his hand. "Right, Pens," he told me, "Time to go meet your Nana!"

Now, I didn't know what a "Nana" was, but if it was anything like the rest of my new life, it was going to be a remarkable and fabulous experience. I "ruffed" at him and play-bowed, stretching my front paws as I lowered my shoulders. Out to the car we went, and Dad lifted me in. We didn't drive very far and pulled into a car park alongside a large building. We got out and walked to the door where Mam pushed a button and we waited until there was a "click" and the door opened. We went down a corridor, where there were rooms of people, some of whom saw me and said how lovely I was. A couple of the people were in uniform and some of them stopped to ask about me and patted me and stroked my head. This was all most acceptable! This must be what "Nana" was; a building full of nice people who would fuss me.

As we continued through the building we came to a door where Dad knocked, and then we went inside. It was a big room with huge glass doors that looked out onto a garden. In a chair on my right as I went in sat a tiny, quiet lady. Her eyes lit up when she saw me. "You must be Penny!" she smiled. I lay my head on her lap and she stroked me and rubbed my ears.

"Penny, this is your Nana," Mam said. I smiled to myself – Nana wasn't a thing, nor a place, but a person! "Hello Nana," I said, rubbing my head against her. She was ever so little, but she was also very strong; I sensed that despite her size, she had a big spirit; a really big personality. I could tell from her scent that she was Dad's family (all people have their individual scent but you can often tell if people are from the same family) and as he told me in the corridor later, this was his "Mam" which I guessed meant his mother. Dad had brought a fluffy bed with him and set it on the floor in front of the glass doors. Here I settled, and as they talked I went off to sleep.

I woke with a jolt as someone swung the door wide open and brought Nana a tray with tea and toast on it. I recognised the smell of roasted bread and runny butter and went over to Nana. Before I could help her eat it, Dad grabbed my collar. "No, Penny – that's Nana's!" he scolded me. I shrugged, "So? She's so small - she won't eat all of it?"

I went back to the little bed and lay down with a sigh. After what seemed an age (but was probably only minutes) Nana called me over and I gently took the crusts one at a time from her hands and chewed and swallowed them. She was a kind lady and I decided that I loved her too.

Later that week we all went over to visit Nana in her room again and it was lunchtime. On the way Dad had called in to the kitchen of the house where Nana lived and asked about lunch for us. The cook smiled and said that this was not a problem. I sat by Nana and was having a fuss when the door to her room opened and one of the girls came in, carrying a tray with two plates on.

She set one before Nan and the other on the little table by Mam. As she left another lady came in, and gave a plate of food to Dad. I was so excited that I couldn't control myself; I wanted to check out everyone's plates – what was on them? Could I have some? When I went to Nana I had a firm "No!" from Dad and Mam together. So then I went to Mam and I saw she had liver and onions and gravy and mashed potato and swede. I leaned over to have a taste and received a tap on my snout, so I stepped back. OK – I know Dad would let me have some. I turned to him and tried some of his. He said "No!" and I sat back. As he tried to eat I tried to help him, but I don't think he really appreciated my helpfulness. As I put my face towards his plate he held me back with his hand. Mam and Nana just burst out laughing as they watched him trying to hold me back with one hand whilst hastily shovelling food into his mouth with the other. The more he tried to eat, the more I tried to push towards his plate. I gave up in the end and plonked myself down with a huff. I turned to look at Nana and Mam who had tears running down their faces as they had laughed so much. I couldn't understand what had been so amusing! On the plus side, I did eventually get the leftovers as they kept a food bowl for me in Nana's room. Laugh all you like, I thought, as I tucked in to the liver, bacon and vegetables.

Those weeks were so different to my previous existence (I wondered whether I could really call that a "life"). I felt that it was only now that my proper life had begun; my new life full of security, warmth, food and constant love. It was a period of constant firsts too. I met lots of people who came to the house – my house. I had a very sneaky suspicion that although they pretended to come and see Dad and Mam, they were really coming to see me. There was Ian, the fish man, who called every Wednesday, Auntie Sarah who came to cut Dad and Mam's fur – I mean hair – and then some of my very favourites; Auntie Theresa and Uncle Bob. They were friends of Nana's who called in now and again. They were very kind and would bring me treats to eat. One day I went over to see Nana in the afternoon and when we were there the door opened and Uncle Bob came in (with Auntie Theresa of course) and a huge piece of cooked pork meat wrapped in paper!

I pride myself that I am normally quite a calm character but that afternoon the smell of that pork drove me nuts. Humans can't fully appreciate how strong my sense of smell and taste is. The rich caramel flavour of the pork crackling (as I know it's called now) was just beyond all limits and was practically making me feel light-headed. No matter how hard I tried to control myself (and Dad to control me), I just couldn't wait to have some. Bob broke off a small piece and I admit I snatched it from his hand (I missed his fingers, honest). This just made me behave more badly, and I think Dad and Mam cut their visit short to take me home for tea. That pork was given to me as treats for the next few days. Even if I was out in the garden, I could smell that the fridge door had been opened and would run into the kitchen just to see if there was a piece of pork for me!

Watching the Squirrel from my Nana's room

5 - THE VETANDHAIRYMAN

One of my other firsts was a trip to the local vet;
the "Vetandhairyman" as my friend Barry Clarke calls
him (our Barry is a bit of a greyhound internet celebrity
like me, and he lives with his own Mam and Dad and a
human puppy or Hoopup called Felix). I think Barry
means the veterinary surgeon. I love a trip in the car so
thought nothing of a (very short) road trip to the village
when I got out, we went inside a rather large building
that smelled of dogs, cats, disinfectant and worse than
that, nervous wee. Let's be honest – Vets had never
made much of a positive impression from my early days
at the track; so many dogs that had injured themselves
racing or even in training went to the vet (or the vet
came to them if they were too badly hurt) and it very
rarely ended well. Very few were ever seen again. My
canine suspicions were aroused as I remembered my
own operation at Sarah's vets. Behind a high counter sat

two nice ladies. They spoke to Dad and Mam who sat on a seat and I stood in front of them. Alongside me was a terrier. He wasn't too friendly so I just turned my back on him, and pushed myself into Dad's lap. I was surprised when my (new) name was called and I was walked into a room where a tall man stood in a coloured apron - I was by now on full alert. It turned out he was my new Vet. He was very gentle as he examined me - checking every joint, every orifice (eww!), each and every tooth, toe and even my tail! He told them what I already knew – that I was in pretty good health apart from a few old wounds from my days in that field. He pointed out a few insect bites, the marks where the invisible creature had nibbled my ankle and some patches of dry skin. Dad told him that my new diet would fix all that - and get a few kilos on me. I was, apparently, 25 kilos but would be better around 29 kilos. The Vet even took a sharp needle and stuck it in the scruff of my neck – it didn't hurt, it was less painful than many of those insect bites.

He said he was a bit concerned about my teeth; years of rubbishy, sloppy food at the kennels and track had apparently not done them any good. It had resulted in me learning not to crunch and chew things, and I had the habit of bolting my food down. I knew that this was wrong, but when you're one of six dogs in a pen and the bowls are pushed in, you learn to get the food down you faster than the next dog. No matter how much Dad tried to encourage me to slow down it was something that had by now become hard-wired. The result was that bits of food gathered around my teeth and decayed, which in turn ate into my teeth.

"That's ok," Dad replied, "We'll start brushing her teeth." I smiled at them all, not understanding or fully appreciating what this actually meant.

Mam picked up a box of something in reception as we left the vets and we went home for our tea. I can't exactly remember what tea was, but I'm sure it was some sort of culinary extravaganza which included kibble. I did try and crunch some of it, but my bad eating habit was something I was not entirely in control of. After they had eaten their tea too, Dad came over to me with something in his hand. He had a blob of something on his finger, which he told me was chicken flavour. I sniffed it. Yeah, right - that had never been anywhere near a chicken in its life, whatever it was! Still, it didn't taste too bad. In his other hand there was

a stick with bristles on, and more of that "chicken stuff".
Gently, Dad held my mouth slightly open, put the stick
in and rubbed the bristles and paste up and down the
outside of my teeth. I didn't know what to make of it; it
was not too unpleasant, I just didn't like it. As soon as
he'd got around the outside of all my teeth I closed my
mouth, and pulled my head away. I mean, I was
learning to love the taste and flavour of good food and
now my palate was being contaminated by chicken paste
that didn't taste of chicken. Well, now that was done.
Teeth cleaned – I won't need that again....or so I
thought!

Dad had had to lift me into the car to go to the
vet as I was still scared of my belly pulling where it had
been cut open. The vet had taken a look and confirmed
that the scars had healed really well, and that the hair
was growing back. He suggested that my reluctance was
just in my head, indeed, that I was a bit neurotic! I think
that considering everything that had happened to me
over my life, I was doing pretty well! Yes, like most
greyhounds I do tend to think a lot and worry about
things that most dogs don't consider. Yes, I was
frightened that I'd jump, stretch my tummy and pull
something, open my stitches maybe, even though the vet

said they had long disappeared.

The stairs were the first hurdle that Dad and Mam got me over; I knew how to get up there in a mad rush of flailing legs, and how to come down with Dad and Mam propping me up and prompting me to move. What I wanted was to be able to go up and down on my own. Dad had an idea that involved one of my favourite foods; chopped-up sausages! Dad put a piece of sausage on each step and then let me go up the stairs. As I had to pause to eat the sausage, it meant that I moved up one step at a time. Over a few days, the sausage was put on every other step, then every third, then every fourth step. In a week I'd learned to go up sensibly.

Coming back down was a different matter; having long, muscular back legs that usually did most of the work, meant I was inclined (no pun intended!) to lift my backside too high and almost somersault down the stairs. Mam suggested that we do the same sausage trick, but the other way. I still had to have Dad in front in case I did something daft, but over the space of a week (and several sausages!) I learned to control my legs, weight, and balance properly. I soon had the skill and confidence to go both up and down safely and confidently.

One lovely, sunny afternoon not long after (it must have been a weekend as both Mam and Dad were home), I'd eaten a wonderful lunch, had a cuddle on the settee and a sit in the warmth of a sun puddle in the main room. I was so very happy that I thought I would just explode. Some days are just like that – so good that you want everyone to know how happy you are. It's difficult to make everyone realise that you are so happy with your lot, that everything is perfect, you are so contented and love it all. We speak different languages, my humans and I, though over time I can understand some of their words and they can understand some of mine too. Dad had gone upstairs so I ran up after him. I spun around in the bedroom and leapt up on the bed, spun around again and jumped off. I ran down the corridor to the other bedroom and jumped up on that bed, then jumped down and ran back to the first bed. I barked as I sped past Dad and Mam (who had now also come up to see what the commotion was). I bounced onto the bed and lay down, shattered. That's when I stopped to listen to what they were saying and I realised, like them, that I'd jumped up on the bed - for the first time without any pain. They both praised me and cuddled me as we all understood what that meant; I could get in and out of the car easier, without having to be lifted. It was a huge mental hurdle for me. Later that day I ran upstairs again, but was hesitant until Dad threw a dog biscuit on the bed - then I followed it. It was a fantastic day – neurotic indeed! The next day I got into and out of the car without having to be lifted, merely encouraged with a dog treat. The world was now my oyster and Dad wouldn't now give himself a hernia!

I got to know the Vet quite well over the following years. I don't like the Vets; I have tried but I just don't like them. They're very nice to me when I go there, but I still don't trust them. I went there once to have my teeth cleaned (remember the "toothpaste" thing? Well, that never worked) and when I woke up, all I had was a mouth full of blood, swollen gums, and only seven teeth left. The vet had stolen the rest and that's why I don't trust them – they'll take the other five if I'm not careful.

That had all started when I felt a bit off my game; I couldn't say what it was, but I didn't feel one hundred percent right. I had a gripey tummy and my mouth itched a lot. Some mornings my mouth felt sore.

I didn't feel much like walking, though I did push myself for a ride in the car. I didn't know how to tell them that something was not quite right - I felt that I was well but not as well as I could have been, if you understand me? Dad picked up on it when he noticed that I was not playing as much. Then when I went lost the edge off my appetite – and I love my food – they took me to the Vet.

The Vet checked me over and asked if my breath was always this bad. Dad replied that it was, due to my mangy, ex-track teeth, typical of an ex-racing greyhound. He was brushing my teeth nearly every day (which I could vouch for – yuck!) but it wasn't helping. He wondered if that's what was affecting my tummy. The Vet agreed that it could cause stomach and liver problems and a "general malaise". A couple of my front teeth were a bit loose too, so it was agreed that I needed a dental – take out one or two of the small front teeth and give the others a clean. The vet actually pointed out that there was a gap in the gum under one of the front teeth already.

I went in a week later and Dad left me in the examination room, from where I was led off to one of the crates at the back of the building. I was feeling very nervous as I could smell the soap, and the anaesthetic though the nurses were very kind to me, and checked on me during the day. I heard them say that I was having my dental about three o'clock. (I don't wear a watch and can't tell the time anyway, except when its dinner time!). I dozed fitfully all day until they came to take me out.

I had my front leg shaved, they put in a needle, and then I drifted off to sleep. The rest of what happened I heard from Mam and Dad after they had collected me. They had rung at half past four to see how I was and were told that I was still in surgery, so to try again in an hour. They rang at half past five and I was still in surgery – Dad nearly had a fit! They rang once more at seven o'clock and were told I was out, in recovery, and that they could collect me about eight o'clock. I was coming around from my deep sleep when I saw Dad walking into the room. I was so pleased and excited to see the both of them but I was so dazed that I could hardly stand. I was dribbling and the nurse was wiping my mouth. All I could taste was the bitter anaesthetic stuff and the metallic taste of blood. I staggered towards Dad who wrapped his arms around me to embrace me, and carefully led me out to the car where he lifted me into the back. I could walk, very wobbly, but everything was spinning round and I was so incredibly tired. From what the nurse had told them, and I overheard, I had had my dental where they had taken out the small teeth. As they cleaned the others they found that most of them were rotten too and had to come out. This was due to years of rubbish food and no chewing. Despite Mam and Dad trying to brush them they were beyond saving. I was left with my four canines and three others (two years later I lost another two so I am now down to five teeth).

I got home and stumbled drunkenly up the drive to the front door. My legs were all going in different directions, despite what I tried to tell them to do. Once in the living room I knew I needed a wee, so with Mam and Dad's guidance I made it to the kitchen door and down to my lawn. Afterwards, I staggered back to the living room and to my special place behind the chair, where Mam had laid out my soft blanket on my duvet and some towels. I was still dribbling blood and saliva as I lay there where I had flopped. They watched over me and wiped my face and mouth. Mam squirted little drops of water into my mouth to keep my tongue moist, but also to rinse some of the blood out. I was so tired but I felt sick too - I was starving hungry but, in spite of that, I was too woozy and dizzy to eat.

I drifted back to sleep. I awoke in the night to find Dad on his chair beside me, keeping an eye on me. My mouth was aching like someone was squeezing it with metal bands and was tearing at it with knives. The vet had given me painkillers but Dad saw they were wearing off. He gave me a little bowl of food which I managed to sit up and eat. It was cereal with some milk and, you know – it tasted like the best meal I had ever eaten! He then carefully slipped two tablets in my mouth – they were wrapped in a small piece of ham and I swallowed them down. He told me they would do me good, but I didn't understand - I just wolfed down the ham as I was starving. I went back to sleep when the pain began to ease, looking up at Dad who was watching over me as my eyelids grew heavy and slowly closed.

By breakfast time I had just about stopped bleeding, but I was still dribbling a lot. I was eating often and, despite my lack of teeth, I was managing. The pain was severe and seemed to come over me in waves. Whenever I could, I just slept. I ate small meals of quite soft food (not a problem for my dental health now as I had very few teeth left to rot!). Mam kept telling me how important it was to eat and drink - not only to keep my strength up, but because it also helped to clear the dried blood and muck from my mouth.

When I was dragged, VERY reluctantly, back to see the vet she was really pleased with how my mouth was healing, and how I was recovering. My eyes were brighter and now the pain was gone I did feel a lot better in myself. That strange feeling that I'd had where I just could not be bothered to do things was gone and both Mam and Dad agreed that I was my old self again. Having only four canines and three tiny pre-molars was a bit of an inconvenience when trying to shovel up my food, and crunching was a bit of a no-no, but I was learning to cope pretty well. Soft food was pretty much the order of the day; sardines (in tomato sauce or plain was fine), pasta, rice, potatoes, ham, any meat with gravy. And I could still have sausages! The vet said that in time my gums would harden and that I would manage to eat most things, even some crunchy ones. That was great – the only difficulty I had was catching things with the gap where my front teeth had used to be!

Back to the subject of Vets. I never minded my Annual vaccinations and other boring stuff but dentals – as you see, they were a whole other matter. I did have a problem with arthritis in my feet – jumping in and out of the car I think doesn't help! After one particular bout of limping, I went to "You-Know-Where" and they said it was joint damage due to racing, and a touch of arthritis. "Laser treatment" was suggested. Dad thought this meant a huge laser to cut my feet off but we were told that is was just a warm light to reduce swelling, to be carried out over a few months.

My first session was with one of the nurses who was very gentle despite me being really worried. How many teeth would I lose this time? Were my toes going the way of my old teeth? The nurse held my paw gently and waved this little light over my wrists on both front feet. It was nicely warm and did not hurt at all. Just as I was getting comfortable she told me that it was over, but I would need to come back in a week. I had a load of these, and I think it did help as my joints were less clicky and definitely less sore. I enjoyed it because the nurses would try to be the ones to do my laser sessions as they all loved how calm and gentle I was (despite me dripping my runny nose in one nurse's face!).

As you can imagine, I am well known at our vets and they all say hello when they see me. When I had to stay in for a blood test and Dad dropped me off, I was taken to the biggest kennel in the room. When Dad came to collect me later I was lying like a Queen on thick blankets and bedding. They had looked after me so well and each of them had come to check me in turn, and given me a cuddle.

Then on one visit I was told by Dad that I was going to have my own passport. This was intriguing. Apparently, we were all going together on a long trip in the big white van. I haven't really mentioned the van yet, so before I talk about the long trip, I'll tell you a bit more about it.

I've already mentioned earlier the van that my trainer owned, which he used to take dogs to the track in. I'd expected the one outside my new home to be the same but how wrong I was! One morning Dad told me that all of us were going out in it for a road trip and a walk. There was a lot of excitement in the house as they both rushed around collecting jackets, bags and other bits, and then ran in and out taking them to the van. Dad put my lead on me and took me down the drive to the opened side door on the van. There was a step which folded out, which I was unsure about, so Dad went inside and called me. I hesitated at first, imagining crates and darkness and the smell of frightened dogs. I gathered up my courage and leapt in (without even the need of a sausage!) and was astonished, for in here there was light, warmth and, best of all, settees! I couldn't believe that there was such luxury. I could sit on my haunches, put my head on the back of the settee and look out of the windows at the people and dogs going by.

I was called off the settee and had to sit on my dog bed behind the seats where Mam and Dad sat. I didn't know where we were going to, but I couldn't wait to get there! The van started with a rumble, then we were off! I was used to car journeys, but this was different. There was so much room, maybe a bit too much at times as it made me worry about rolling round, even though I never did.

When we arrived at our destination, I stood up and walked between the seats to look out to see where we were. What was there at this new place? I could see trees, lots of grass, some people and I could smell animals and dogs. I couldn't wait to get out and explore.

Mam said something about having a cup of tea, but I knew I needed a walk first – I even barked at them to tell them to hurry up. She shrugged, "Lets take the girl out first or we'll have no peace!"

I jumped down onto the grass amongst lots of cars. I could hear dogs barking and human pups shrieking and shouting. All this did was make me keener to see what was going on and what I was missing out on. This place was amazing – we walked for a while and I sniffed to see who'd been there and weed to tell other dogs that I'd been here too. Back at the van, I climbed back in and sat up on the settee. There was even a cooker and fridge in here and they made something to eat. Dad shared his meat sandwich with me, and I had a drop of milk with water in it. I was offered some kibble but, to be honest, I was so excited by all the noise and smells that it didn't interest me.

After our food, we had a longer walk up into the trees of an ancient wood. At one point I was sure that I saw a small black greyhound looking at me through the trees but when I looked again they had gone. That was odd. Neither Dad nor Mam seemed to have seen her, just me. We had a little more food when we got back to the van. It was a wonderful experience with everything I loved; food, adventures and somewhere to sit in comfort. I tried to stay awake on the way home but I was asleep by the time we had reached the main road. I dreamt of food, comfy beds, walks in green grass and a black dog that winked at me.

We began to take more and more trips in the van. It was great – every trip was an adventure and once or twice we met up with friends. We even went on a couple of trips where there were lots of greyhounds. That was exciting as we all spoke the same language, knew how to react to each other and could exchange stories about what our humans did. I heard such things - and I'd thought mine were weird!

Once or twice we stayed out overnight and even slept in the van. This was really fantastic; at 9 o'clock the settees would disappear and a huge bed was pulled out and made up with duvets and cushions and pillows. I was so excited about the big bed that Mam had to hold me back or I would jump on it before all the bedding came out. This was very cool, all of us sleeping together as one big pack. I was not allowed under the blankets (it would have been too hot for me anyway) but I could cuddle up to them on top of the duvets. If it got cold, I had my "Mr Snoozee" blanket to go over me. To a greyhound there could be nothing better than sleeping with your family.

My usual pose in the van!

Or just wistfully dreaming the day away....

6 - CLEVER PENNY!

I love my Auntie Wendy. She says I'm clever. I am too. When I'd been with them a few months I was taken to "dog school" which was held once a week in a building not too far from where Nana lived. I remember it was along a street where there were dozens of lumps in the road designed to slow the car down and make me bang my head on the roof or against the tailgate as I looked out the window. Either way, I don't approve of lumpy roads. When we arrived, I had to wait in the car with Mam when Dad went inside, then when he came back out we all went in together. I think I was four and a half years old at that stage and only six months off the track. Inside there were people and dogs – all tiny little dogs, barely older than puppies. Here we had to learn to sit, lie down, and stay and just get along with the other dogs - Auntie Wendy said that this was most important of all. I was the biggest dog there by far. On one occasion we were all sitting in a row when a new dog came to the class and the owner was being introduced to us. The conversation went something like; "This is Fluffy, he's eleven months, this is Spike, he's just over a year, and this [steps back to take in my size] is Penny, she's four and a half".

I was only in the puppy class for a couple of months before I went up to the Advanced Class. Here I started as the Dunce. All the others knew how to do the sit stays, downs, even the retrieves, but I couldn't. I didn't like it when Dad walked away from me and I would follow, which was wrong apparently. I could sometimes see the despair and disappointment on their faces when I didn't get it right. I really did want to learn, to make Dad and Mam proud of me, and to hear Auntie Wendy the dog trainer say "watch how Penny does it." The other dogs were very nice, but one or two of the clever ones used to snigger at me and talk about me amongst themselves. I couldn't help it. I wanted to be good but I was a self-conscious worrier.

Until one day Dad told me to sit – and I did – and he walked away, and I waited, and waited, and when he turned to me I ignored the urge to run to him. I waited that little bit longer until he said, "Penny, come!" so I did. I ran up the room, and stopped in front of him. I heard Auntie Wendy call out to the class, "Isn't Penny a clever girlie!" I was beaming. Apparently some greyhounds can't sit but Dad said that all theirs have, and Sammy their little black greyhound was also brilliant at obedience.

Later in that class, Auntie Wendy needed a volunteer to demonstrate how to walk properly and I was straining on my lead, thinking "Pick me! Pick me!" and she did. I was so pleased to be showing all the other clever-clogs how to walk properly on a lead, and how to do it all quietly and politely without any barking or snippy canine comments. Over the following weeks the dogs changed, and I got better and more confident, I became one of the stars of the obedience class. I even learned to retrieve which was a bit of a leap for a greyhound (apparently we don't retrieve by nature as we are too independently minded). Whereas collies, Labradors and spaniels will just do it – go and fetch something thrown for them – sighthounds generally don't understand. I mean, if your owner wanted something that badly, why did they throw it away in the first place? Common sense, isn't it? I liked it when they rolled the ball for me – I would chase it, as it was something moving across the ground. When they threw it in the air – not so interesting. One week, one of my friends (a spaniel called Rusty) had a squeaky ball which he would run after and catch, squeak it and bring it back. Now, that one really got to me, and I got excited when the ball rolled and squeaked. By the next week Dad had bought me the same squeaky ball and I couldn't help but chase after it. I learned that if I took it back to Dad he would give me a treat, and then roll it away so that I could chase it again. This was a fun thing to do, so I did.

The next weekend we went to a local park where there was a fenced off court area, and we practiced here for a while. It was only about ten minutes, but that was long enough for me to go through my routine, though not so long that I got bored. We would even practice routines at home, in the living room. I learned to stay, wait, then come to Dad, sit in front of him, then walk around him to sit by his side. This was called a "finish". I love doing this, and we still do when we go to talks and things.

The big field behind the house, the one where I was so wary of walking when I first came home (they

call it The Cricket Pitch) doesn't scare me any more.
Dad used to walk me there every morning when he
worked in the city, and he would take my squeaky ball.
He would roll it for me and I would run off and bring it
back for a treat. Sometimes, he would throw it across
the grass as far as he could and I would launch myself
after it. He trusted me to come back and I always did
(though I would occasionally stop for a sniff and a wee
on the way). I would sometimes grab the ball and do a
full circuit of the pitch before coming back to him and
dropping the ball in his hand, as I had been taught to do
at Auntie Wendy's class. That moment when you are
first trusted to go off the lead on your own is a very
important thing for me as a dog, and for Dad as my
family. It's a great responsibility on us both. I have
always tried my very best not to let ourselves down.

That was until the morning when he threw the
ball and it bounced, and smacked me on the nose. I
yelped, and, holding the ball tightly between my teeth, I
went home. I knew the route and stopped every now and
again to check that Dad was following me (he is not as
fast as me, him only having two short legs). When I got
to the front door I waited for him, and gave him my ball
just before going inside. Auntie Wendy would have

been so proud of me!

Even now I like to have a stretch and a run when I can. I have to keep myself fit. My favourite exercise is to run up and down the stairs to and from my bed (sorry – their bed!).

I like to keep my mind occupied; I love toys that I have to work at to get the food out. I have a number of different ones that you have to work in different ways; Bluey is triangular and rolls along the floor, I have a Kong that you have to drop or throw on the floor and I have another that you chew to break up the treats inside. What I could never understand was those fluffy toys with a squeak inside. What was the point of them? I had a triangular fluffy one that had no squeak left as the dogs before me had killed it; I liked that one until one day my tooth got caught in it and I tore it apart. I had other squeaky toys that didn't interest me. Then a few months back my Auntie Pam (Pam and Dave are friends of my Mam and Dad who live with Lolly and Lulu, two greyhound friends of mine) gave me a fluffy toy that Dad and Mam named Missy Moo (I think it's supposed to be a cow). Anyway, I think Lolly might have played with it as it smelled of her and when I sniffed it I got the

urge to chew it and throw it around. Over the year
Auntie Pam has brought me loads of fluffy toys and I
think I might actually have realised why they are so
much fun. Some of them are soft, and I like to cuddle
them, and others I just like to squeak and fling around,
mostly when its food time and they are ignoring me. I
have even taken to falling asleep on Missy Moo and
Baabara my sheep. Odd how your habits can change as
you get older.

When I first came to live with them I slept in the
kitchen, and this went on for a few months as I was quite
comfortable there. After a while I realised that I enjoyed
being with Mam and Dad so much that I wanted to be a
bit closer to them, so I started crying and chewing on the
kitchen door with my little front teeth (before the Vet
stole them). They put up with this for a few weeks but
they then allowed me to sleep in the living room. It was
warmer and cosier here, and I would sleep on my grey
bed beside Dad's chair, where it smelled of them. I
wasn't allowed on the furniture at the beginning either
but I sneaked up now and again, so they began to allow
me to lie on my own blanket on the settee. This was
lovely. It was only a matter of time before I was caught
sleeping on the settee at night!   They were very good

about it – Dad said that I was well behaved and clean so they would cut me a bit of slack. They didn't see me chuckling to myself over that! The first holiday that we all had together in the motorhome, when the big bed was rolled out, we all slept alongside each other as a pack. Fabulous! When we came home, there was no way I was going too sleep on the settee downstairs on my own; I slept up on the bed with them.

With my fractious nerves, and the fear caused by heavy rain, I have found that curling up in the dog bed in the kitchen works to soothe me and make me feel safe. I can wrap myself in a blanket. Maybe it's because the bed smells faintly of two of their old dogs. One of those dogs often keeps me company – I know that sounds odd.

Remember I mentioned the black dog that I saw in the woods? I had seen her out of the corner of my eye that time but I had picked up her scent too. I recognised it as I have, on occasion, seen and smelled her at home. One evening as I lay on the settee after Dad and Mam had gone to bed, I was drifting off to sleep and I caught a faint, familiar smell of dog - like the smell on my kitchen bed. I opened my eyes to find a slight black greyhound stood in front of me, smiling. I smiled back and asked her who she was. She said that her name was Sammy and that this was her home. I was puzzled, and said that this was my home, but I had never seen her here before. She explained that she didn't live here any more but she kept an eye on her Mam and Dad and now on me too, to make sure that things were ok. She told me she missed them very much, and her Nana who was now living in the Nursing Home. I nodded – I had a Nana in the Nursing Home too! "Yes," Sammy told me, "it's the same Nana – she's your Nana now." She asked me to look after her Mam and Dad, and said that they were good people who would do everything to protect me. That's when I realised that my Dad and Mam were Sammy's parents and that the photo on the bookcase of their last greyhound was Sammy. We spoke for a little while, and she told me about the rainbow bridge.

Sammy explained to me that when we leave this earth, when we are old or broken and cannot live any more, we cross the rainbow bridge to a place where we are healed and young again. There all our friends and family wait for us until it's our time to go there too. Sometimes hounds and humans can cross back to watch over those who loved them, and she said that she was one of those lucky angel hounds. She nuzzled me a "Goodnight" and

I went back to sleep. I haven't spoken to this angel hound since but I still see her sometimes, watching over us.

I wonder if Sammy knows any of my friends? Gabe and Henry Henry have gone across the rainbow bridge and I miss them. There are many others as well – including dear Popsy who was my very best friend. When I went to stay with my Auntie Kerry and Uncle Mike for my holidays I would sleep with Popsy either beside me or just touching paws. Henry Henry was there for the first few of my holidays at Kerry's but he was old and not very well and by the next time I visited he had gone. He was a real gentleman, so very polite, and he had a nose that wobbled when he got excited, as did his back legs. Popsy was old too, but despite her kidney problems she lived to a good age for a greyhound. I wish Sammy would come and tell me how they are - I guess she is now busy spending time with our Nana who I miss so much too. Nana passed over the bridge not long ago and I miss my visits to see her and help her eat her food. What I really miss most of all is her laugh.

Practicing my retrieves on the cricket pitch

7 - EURO PENNY

So, going back to the "Long Journey" I
mentioned earlier. I had to go to the Vet in order to have
more injections before we could go, and I even had to
get my own passport. I was a bit unsure what a passport
was, but Dad tried to explain that it was what humans
needed when they went for very long journeys, and now
dogs could have them too.   I was a bit suspicious at
first at the thought of a "long journey" in the van. I
guess I still had at the back of my mind being abandoned
in a field. No matter how much I settled, how much they
loved me, I still worried about it all coming to an end
and being left alone again.

The preparations were incredible (Dad described
it as being like a "Military Operation", whatever that
meant); I watched loads of food, bedding and more food
being taken out to the van. I saw a dog bed taken out

(yeah – as if I was sleeping in that!), some bags of kibble and boxes of cereal (by now I'd graduated from crunchy cornflakes with nuts to porridge). There were more clothes than I'd ever thought they owned – whole wardrobes seemed to have been emptied as the contents went out to the van. I was puzzled as to what weather we were expecting; presumably every type imaginable! The week went by until it was time for us to eventually leave (at last!).

Surprisingly, there was still enough room in the van for us! I insisted that I had three of my best jackets with me; a fleece, a light waterproof and my lined waterproof. That would cover my needs - as long as there was enough porridge I'd suffer the rest. My travelling bed was set behind the front seats and my lead attached to the arm rests so that I couldn't wander down the van, but had to sit behind Mam on my bed (I'd not yet discovered how to jump on the settees and hold on whilst travelling). There was a lot of them getting in and out, swopping the car round, locking doors – enough to make me very bored indeed. Eventually, at long last, and after an age, we drove off. All I could think was that if it took this amount of time to get out of the house, how long would this "long" journey eventually turn out to be!

I watched the road that we lived on disappear. We passed where Nana lived, onto the long wide road that one way led to the rescue kennels and the other led to adventures. I stood up a few times and looked out of the front window, at cars and lorries passing us, as we passed others. The van was going quite fast now - on we continued - I assumed my usual position and slept.

We had a couple of short stops for them to toilet and me too, and we stretched our legs a bit. Both times they were great, noisy car parks with lorries and cars but there was grass and trees for me to sniff and wander through. I met a pug and we said hello politely. He was on a long journey too, but he was going up north. I understood from what Dad and Mam had been saying that we were heading south and over the sea. I'd only been on the sea once, on the way from Ireland and I hadn't liked it as I'd been sea-sick in that dirty, smelly van; it had never been as comfortable as on this journey.

Back in the van and away we went again. I dozed off once more, to be woken by Mam gently calling my name; we had arrived at our first overnight stop. Dad took my lead and we stepped down onto grass, where I stood and looked around. There were many vans lined up; some with people sat beside them at tables with umbrellas, and others with umbrellas that were actually attached to their vans. There were also dogs, some being walked and others sitting with their families outside their vans – under those very umbrellas. It was lovely and open and I could smell salt air – I recognised the smell of the sea from our trips to the beach. The sea was nowhere to be seen – it must be a few miles away, I guessed.

We ate a lovely meal and had a proper mooch around the site afterwards. There was an interesting dog walk which took us out onto the flat farmland that spread around our campsite. We sauntered around this for a while until I decided I wanted to go back to the van as I could feel it was nearly 9 o'clock so time for tea and biscuits in bed (I would occasionally partake of a few ginger biscuits dunked in tea or coffee). It had been a good day and walking back in the Kent summer evening sunshine was a great way to end that day's adventures. Before they had turned out the lights after supper I was already fast asleep, starting to kick my legs in a dream. Whatever would the next day bring?

Dad shook me gently about six o'clock to tell

me that it was time for breakfast and to put the bed away. "What?" I thought, "It's still night time!" The sun was up and light streamed through the glass panel in the roof. I was sleepy as I ate my breakfast. I'd been up in the night for three o'clock wees and Dad had walked me up the site and then back to the van. Now breakfast was finished I needed another toilet stop but I had to cross my legs until they had folded the bed away, and the duvets and pillows too. I only had to go a few vans before I did what I needed to do, but we had a small walk to get some air as Dad said that the next part of the journey might be a long one. Back in the van Mam had washed and dressed, Dad put on his travelling clothes and then the cables were unhooked and tucked away and the outside gas was turned off. It was time to go!

Getting out onto the main road was somewhat awkward, the lanes were rather narrow with high hedges and even I had to close my eyes on a couple of occasions as I could imagine the door mirrors being knocked off. Yet, we survived intact! We were on the wide roads by now, half an hour before arriving at a huge set of buildings where there were many, many cars, lorries and coaches. I had to get out for a wee and I nearly jumped out in front of a coach, but Dad grabbed my harness tightly and held me back. That was close! Safely back inside the van we stopped and started a few more times, before we went into a long, dark tunnel; I wasn't really frightened, though I was a bit unsure. Dad explained that this was a coach on top of a train that would take us through a tunnel under the sea. I didn't know whether the explanation was for mine or Mam's benefit!

Eventually doors whirred and clanged, it became dark and we started to move. Dad and Mam were in the back with me on the settees, drinking tea (them, not me!). I did sit tight up to Dad for reassurance as the carriage rattled and shook, moving quite fast through the darkness. I know that I was not so much worried as concerned but I didn't puff or pant, just pushed myself harder against him. We had the lights on in the back of the van and it was quite comfortable, apart from the movement; we even had the CD player on playing music I liked. It wasn't long before it became light outside again, I was clipped back in my travelling bed and they sat down in their seats ready to start the engine when they were told to by the people in charge on the train. The carriage stopped, the huge metal and glass doors that had clanged shut when we boarded now rattled open, the vans in front of us moved and we followed them out onto the lanes which led upwards and onto more roads. I have to say that even though I was wary, I was also very curious and found it interesting.

We stopped once at an enormous supermarket for them to buy food (as if there wasn't already a tonne of food on board!) and I had a comfort break myself, then we were back on the road once more.

"Next stop Brugge!" Dad announced. Mam cheered and I smiled. I didn't know where Brugge was, but apparently we were well on the way. I stood to watch out of the front of the cab. I realised that we were going the wrong way – on the wrong side of the road and I tried to nudge Dad with my nose, but he seemed to be sure of what he was doing, so I settled back on my travelling bed and crossed my paws for good luck.

I was wondering; Dad had spoken to a few people on the way but in a different language to normal. I understood the tone but the words were different. I looked puzzled, but he had explained that we were now in a different country where people spoke different languages. That made me think – did dogs in different countries speak different languages? Or did we all just speak dog, but with an accent? I knew that greyhounds had different mannerisms to other breeds and used different sounds sometimes. Maybe foreign greyhounds were poles apart from me language-wise?

The road was pretty straight and it was some time before the voice in the box on the front window told us that we were to "take the next exit!" Now this is something I just have to tell you about; they have a little person who they call "Dora" that lives in a black box that sits on the front window of the van. She is quiet most of the time but then she will all of a sudden tell us (very loudly) where we are and where she wants us to go. It scared the heck out of me when Dora first shouted directions to us, but now I ignore her, pretty much as they do! She often tells them (and she repeats herself) to go one way, but they go another. She never seems to lose her temper or get miffed because they've ignored her, but she really does go on and on to try and get them to change course and go where she wants them to go. She must be very small, but she is very clever as she seems to know where everywhere is. Most of the time. So here we were, turning off the big road towards the town we were staying in for a few nights – Brugge.

Despite Dora's directions, Dad and Mam were

having a disagreement over which would be the best way to go. Evidently Dora was wrong, as she kept repeating for them to turn left when they went straight on. I stood up to look around; we were in the middle of a very built up square, surrounded by high buildings and full of hundreds of people milling around. There was a bit of tension in the cab as I could tell that ignoring Dora had not been a great idea; Dad announced that we were in the middle of the "Bloody Markplatz in a motorhome!" From the tone of his voice I don't think that was a good thing. Still, despite his muttering, they managed to get back off the square and onto the road.

"Look! There's the sign for the campsite – Camping Memling!" Mam pointed. Dad slowed, turned right and then left, down a street of nice houses and trees. They pulled into our new campsite and parked up. Dad went in to book our pitch. He was soon out, and we drove round the small park to our own spot. Mam laughed as it was the same spot that they had stayed at a couple of years before!

The hook-up was in, the CD player on, kettle boiling, and it was time for a cup of tea (I had noticed that this was some sort of ritual that whenever the van stopped and they put the handbrake on, then almost always the kettle went on next). I was bursting to both explore and have a wee, so I tried to remind them by squeaking politely. Before the tea was poured I had my way, was on my lead and we were trotting around the site. The vans were parked closely here, not like the places we had usually stayed at. Everyone was friendly, including a very rotund yellow Labrador, who ambled out of his caravan to say hello. He said that his name was Klaus and that he lived in Holland (which was the country next door) and I told him that I was from Wales. He wasn't sure where that was, so I explained that it was across the sea. He nodded, but I still don't think he was entirely sure what I meant. This had answered my question – they all spoke dog, but indeed with a bit of an accent. However, I couldn't stop to chat as Dad seemed to be in a hurry. Off we continued through a wooden gate which led into a wood that smelled of trees, mud and of dogs! We had a lovely walk in the small forest, having to jump out of the way at one stage as a jogger and his Alsatian companion sped past us. I really enjoyed this stretch of my legs, which was much needed after the long drive to Brugge. We came back to the campsite along a street of houses, past where we had stopped for Dad to register us. We had only been out for about an hour, but it was just perfect to blow the cobwebs off and unwind; by the time we climbed back in the van I was ready for a nap. I jumped up on my favourite settee, but Dad was already sitting there. I sat and looked down at him. He sighed and moved over, so I squeezed myself into the gap between him and the back of the seat, stretched out and fell asleep. I woke a little later to the sound of Dad snoring next to me. I smiled, snuggled up and went back to sleep.

"Time for food!" Mam called, waking both Dad and I with a jolt. I wasn't much good at cooking, but I was great at supervising. On holidays, Dad cooked, so I followed him outside and sat to watch him cooking some bacon on a tiny gas stove that they had bought for this trip. "Saves making the inside of the van stink of bacon," Dad told me. I shrugged – I couldn't see the problem with the heavenly scent of freshly cooked, crispy bacon.

Inside, Mam was cooking pasta and had opened a puttanesca sauce. I was disappointed that the cheese was just a cheddar and not a nice Parmigiano Regiano or a Grana Padano. I have become something of a connoisseur over the years and even a bit of a food snob; how I've changed from the days I was happy to guzzle down slop at the track kennels! Dad often says that he can't understand how they expected to get a good performance out of me by feeding me rubbish – its like trying to run a sports car on two-star fuel he says. Once the bacon was nice and crispy (I was thinking it was a bit burnt!) it was chopped up and they had it with the pasta and sauce with cheese grated on top. I had some dried food (kibble) with pasta, chopped bacon, sauce and cheese too. A lovely way to end a lovely day. Naturally, I cleared my bowl – well, it was the polite thing to do after all! They went to the main block to wash the dishes whilst I lay on the settee, head on the back, watching them work so hard whilst I guarded the van. When they came back, we sat outside for a while and I enjoyed the evening sunshine, until it was nearly 9 o'clock and it was time for the bed (and tea and biscuits) to come out..

Dad and Me on the Markplatz, Brugge

Me waiting patiently for my waffles

8 - IN BRUGES (OR BRUGGE)

The sun had risen and was warming the windscreen of the van quite early the next morning. I was awake, but I didn't want to get up yet – unless it was for breakfast. They were both fast asleep, so I squiggled between them, rolled on my back and dozed on. By the time I woke next, Mam had gone off to the toilet and Dad was sitting up. Breakfast!

After my morning amble through the woods, we collected Dad's camera and Mam's handbag and set off for town. Brugge is a big town. I knew this from our drive in the day before – so I imagined that a walk into town was going to take a long time and involve an awful lot of walking. I didn't expect us to stop so soon – just a few hundred yards from the campsite we halted under a metal post with writing on it. It was too far up for me to see and, anyway, I couldn't read!

We'd only stood around for ten minutes or so and a small van stopped by the post – a van with lots of seats and people inside. The door opened and Dad went in, said something in a strange language, and Mam and I followed. The people in the van looked at me and most of them smiled, and as there were no free seats I stood next to Dad, who tucked me in as far I could go. The bus, as it was called, stopped and started many times as it made it's journey. Each time it stopped people got on or off the bus. All of them looked at me. One of them asked Dad about me in their strange language but Dad answered in our own language which the other man seemed to understand. As they spoke, people around us on the bus listened and one or two nodded and others smiled. Eventually, Mam and Dad stood up, as did I, and we wobbled unsteadily on our feet as the bus came to a halt.

We stepped down into a busy street full of shops, bustling with people and noisy with lots of voices and traffic. I stuck close to Dad as we walked along the narrow pavement, until we reached a shop window where we stopped and Mam pointed; in the window was a picture of greyhounds like me! Mam held me when Dad went inside. He spoke to the shopkeeper who went over and took the picture from the window – it wasn't a picture but a cushion. It was put in a bag, Dad said goodbye and came out with it. We crossed the road in between buses and cars and towards the shop Mam had been talking about for days; L'Occitane, her very favourite shop in the entire world (apparently). She went inside and then beckoned to Dad who pointed to me, but the lady behind the counter smiled and beckoned us inside too. Into the shop I went, towards the lady who came out from behind the counter to make a fuss of me. "Ahh – a windhund," she said, kneeling to look into my face. "Wind hound," I thought. "That's a bit personal!" The lady said that she had a greyhound just like me. Dad asked about dogs being allowed in shops in this city, and the lady said that most shops here were ok with dogs, as long as they were well behaved. I smiled, as I knew that I was always well behaved. They did some buying in this wonderful place, that smelled of soap, perfume and flowers, then after another cuddle from the friendly lady, we said goodbye and went back onto the pavement. The smells coming down the street were a mixture of flowers, meat and cooking food – the aroma of hams and chickens roasting, cheeses and fresh bread. All my favourite foods in the world, and all so nearby.

Walking up the street away from the bus stop the smells were getting stronger. We came out into a huge, bright, square area that was surrounded by high buildings with pointed fronts. On one side was a building with a high tower and on three sides there were loads of places to eat, like the pubs at home but with seats outside. What astonished me, and was the source of the smells, was that in the middle of the square there were vans, lorries, and cars with coloured tents open to the front where people were selling the most wonderful range of foods, both raw and cooked. There were tables of colourful flowers with heady scents next to stalls where legs of pork were roasting. One van was selling chips (I love chips), another selling something called waffles, and another selling ice-creams. I was mesmerised as we walked through the stalls. I had my head up and my long nose in the air, wrinkling as I drew in the smells; it was a total sensory extravaganza for me. The first time someone stopped to fuss me I was a little surprised, but it happened more and more as we walked further into the square. People came over from all sides to say hello to me and ask about me and what my story was. I heard Dad answering as they asked whether I was Spanish (no, I was Irish but was now Welsh, which seemed to throw them a bit), and they all seemed to know about greyhounds. One of the people explained to us that there was a group of people in Belgium who rescued the Spanish greyhounds, close relatives of mine, who were used for hunting in Spain. They explained that each year huge numbers of them are abandoned (or even worse) when the hunting season is over; for the first time in my life I felt that there was a dog out there that had a life worse than a 'no longer wanted for racing' greyhound. I did enjoy the fuss though and if I could help to promote the plight of greyhounds – Spanish or not – I thought it was a very good thing.

"Right," Dad smiled at me, "I think it's time for lunch!" There was a brief conversation between them as to where to go to eat, but they decided on a nice restaurant opposite the tall tower (Dad called it the "Belfry" and told me it was full of bells). The waiter came over and Dad asked whether it was ok to bring me, and the man smiled and said, "Of course! Would you like a bowl of water for the dog?"

They sat in a corner where it was thought my backside wouldn't knock over any passers-by (as if I would!). They didn't want a large meal as Dad was going to cook that evening, so decided to have something light to eat. They were also very thirsty so when the waiter came back over they asked him to recommend two beers and something light for lunch. He suggested the beers and also waffles with strawberries and cream. Sounded great to me - what would Dad and Mam be having?

When the beers arrived, I laughed, as did Dad; Mam blushed a bit; her beer came in a very long glass in a wooden holder. It was a not an easy thing to drink from and as she tried, people passing the restaurant stopped to watch. You couldn't be shy in Brugge! Dad looked very sensible as he drank his beer from a normal glass. Even more people stopped to look when we ate the waffles; they were lovely – sweet, buttery and crispy, covered in thick cream with strawberries that were so very fresh and smelled of sweet berry flavours. I sat patiently for my share, which is what halted the people. They watched as the elegant black greyhound was hand fed waffles with cream, and then huge chunks of strawberry. Mam did manage to drink nearly all of her beer, as I did my bit and mopped up the last of the waffles. We had an after lunch amble through the market stalls and they bought some cooked meat, cooked potatoes and coleslaw for our evening meal. We walked a bit more around the town, but by then it was mid-afternoon and Mam decided that it was time to make our way back to the campsite.

We didn't have to wait long at the bus stop; the little bus arrived, the door opened and we stepped in. At the next stop a group of young people got in, some of whom were having problems walking, and others couldn't talk. One of them sat on the small seat across the walkway from me. He looked so gentle that I went across and leaned against him. It made the boy smile, I put my head against his chest, and he stroked me. Despite the bus bouncing, stopping and starting, and people getting off and on, I felt that it was important for me to keep this boy company and I did this for most of the journey home. The group got off a couple of stops before us, and the boy gave me a cuddle before he left the bus. If I made one person feel a bit better, then I consider that my day was worthwhile. The people on the bus had watched me and I had made many of them smile too. Dad told me later that I'd made him and Mam so very proud, that it made them feel warm inside and that they had even wiped a tear from their eyes. I just thought they were soppy.

We took a few trips around the area over the next few days, even seeing a tower with lots of arms on they called a windmill. Interesting…but not as much as some of the restaurants we passed by.

We left Brugge and drove south towards a town called Ieper (or Ypres). Just outside we visited a place where there were rows and rows of stones with writing on. The place was called Tyne Cot. I didn't know what this place was, but I could feel that there was a lot of sadness here; Dad explained that every one of these stones was where a dead human was buried, each one who had been killed in a big fight nearly 100 years ago. I couldn't believe that there were so many people or how so many could have been killed in one spot. I looked up at him and asked – 'Why did they die, Dad?' He told me that people from one country wanted to tell people from another country what to do and how to live, and that's what the fighting was all about. This really puzzled me; humans can be so clever - build windmills and make waffles and cream, but they can't just live together. That made me feel sad too, especially as I looked out at all the white stones with writing on, each one once a person.

At Ieper we had a lovely campsite again, this

time on the edge of a small town, with a meadow and patches of trees. We went into town almost as soon as we had arrived. The path to town went through the meadow which was full of rabbits (they were vaguely interesting, though I would rather have chased a strawberry waffle). When we left the meadow the path opened onto a road, on the other side of which was a river, and beyond it a high wall which surrounded the town itself. We walked alongside the river until we came to a wide gateway, where the road went through a fat tower, and into the town centre. We had a little look through the gateway but they said we were all coming back later for the ceremony. I didn't know what that meant, but I felt sure that it would be interesting.

Later that evening we went back towards the great gate; all along the side of the road beside the river many big buses were parked (Dad counted ten), all empty. "Where have all the people gone," I wondered? We saw more and more people as we drew closer to the gates, where Dad and Mam went through the doorway until they were under the tower itself. It was a vast space, full of people, covered by a high arching roof of stone. Here they stood, with me, amongst what must have been hundreds of mostly older people, though there

111

were children there too. As we stood and were silent, men in uniform came in and blew trumpets, and someone else read something out. Despite the crowd of people around me I was perfectly behaved – I could feel how important this was to the people there, and I wanted to show my respect too. As the crowd dispersed, some people came over and said how good I had been; Dad thanked them and said that it was time for my reward for being so well behaved. We walked through into the town and onto the square. It was busy here too, with cars driving around - though not quite as many people as had been under the great gate. Mam looked at the menus that were outside the restaurants and checked them off one by one as we walked down the road towards the centre of Ieper. Eventually Dad said, "This looks like a good one." Mam perused the menu, nodded and they looked inside. Dad went in and asked the owner "Is it ok to bring in the dog?" Once again the reply was, "Of course. Would you like a bowl of water for her?"

Inside it was warm and cosy and smelled of beer, wood smoke and food; we sat in the corner table near the huge front window and I stood there looking at the view across the busy square. Despite it being evening it was still quite light outside and I watched the cars and people jostling by. Some of the people in the restaurant were talking about me and smiling. I grinned happily back. When the gentleman came over with a list of the food and drinks, he patted me too. Dad ordered something like Flaming Stoves (at least that's what it sounded like) and two beers. I settled under the table to wait for the burning cooker to arrive – it sounded exciting, if not a bit dangerous! The beers seemed pretty normal though in different shaped glasses (they seemed to like their odd glassware here) but then the flaming stove arrived – they were huge bowls of beef stew! I could smell the herbs and the rich beef from where I lay, and I really hoped that I might get a taste, as I had been so well behaved. From what Dad was saying to Mam I realised I had misheard what he'd said; this was Vlaamsche Stoverij, which in the local human language was Flemish Stew (that sounded even less appetising than a flaming cooker!). This area was called Flanders and the people were Flemish, hence the name – now that explanation sounded much better! Towards the end of their meal, pieces of beef were passed under the table to me and it truly was as wonderful as it smelled. Dad also dipped some of the crusty bread in the stew, and I had some of that too. It was another magical evening, for all of us.

The people were all so kind and friendly in this town, and we had to stop quite a few times for people to pat me and ask about me. I decided that I liked Flanders as it has wonderful food and lovely people who were interested in us greyhounds. The walk back took us along the high wall that ran alongside the river. The path was very wide and had large areas of lawned grass and many large blocks of stone, cut into strange shapes. They had writing on them; chiselled into the stone, which I couldn't read of course, but Dad read some of them out to Mam and me (though I think it was actually more for my benefit). These were stones that recorded lots more people from around the world who had come here many years ago in that big war that I mentioned earlier. The same war that had created all those grave stones I had seen that day. It made me feel sad for those lives lost – both human and animal – but I was also heartened by the way in which the people had rebuilt their lives and their beautiful town.

9 - FRENCH FIELDS

The next day we had a long journey south, from Flanders to a part of a country called Normandy. Apparently, this is where Mam's family came from. We stopped a couple of times along the way for us to eat, and for us to all have a toilet break. Even though I slept in between stops, I did find the travelling a bit tiring and I was glad to get to the next campsite. The pitch took a bit of jiggling to get into; I supervised from the back seat as Mam shouted directions to Dad from outside as he first reversed, then went forward and reversed again. I winced at one point, as I could see the apple tree getting very close and we hit one of the branches, but only ever so slightly. As soon as the engine was turned off, Dad jumped out and plugged our wires in, opened the outside cupboard to "turn on the gas" and within a few minutes the kettle was on. It was time for food again!

This site was in the middle of countryside –
there were fields behind us, and woods behind them.
We took a walk around after my food and it was a very
pretty site, busy though not full. I met a few dogs on my
walk, most of them from other countries but I did meet a
lady with an English greyhound. We bumped noses and
sniffed each other, with stiff waggy tails, as is polite. He
was a very happy chap, who said we would love it here
as the sausages were brilliant! I only hoped that Dad
and Mam knew about these fabulous sausages.
Fortunately they did!

That evening, we stopped at a wooden building
near the entrance where they spoke to a lady and
gentleman. I distinctly remember Mam mentioning
sausages. We then went for a walk out of the site and up
the quiet road past some houses; everything was so
peaceful, apart from one house where there was a large
and very noisy German shepherd dog, who shouted at us
to keep out of his garden (which we weren't in as we
were out on the road). He needn't have worried about
that, as we stopped and returned to the wooden building
in the campsite, where the man handed Mam two trays
of food; chips and sausages! I practically dragged them
back to the van. The table came out; they opened a

bottle of wine and sat down to eat. I had my own
sausage, which, after they had finished, Dad chopped up
with some kibble and some chips – with ketchup – and
water. I was famished (Mam said that the country air
had given me an appetite!). The English greyhound had
been right – the sausages were fabulous! I cleared my
bowl, of course.

The next morning we walked down through a
thick forest (full of wonderful sniffs and smells) into a
small village. The houses were different here to Brugge
or Ieper; they were made of stone and wood together.
Dad (as usual) had his camera with him and was
stopping all the time to take pictures; whilst I never
minded (it gave me a chance to sniff things) it would
after a while start to drive Mam nuts! I would hear her
tutting and muttering as we hung around, waiting. In the
village was a very large building with a tower. It was an
Abbey (apparently, whatever that was) and parts of it
were very old and, so it appeared, were well worth
photographing. Dad was particularly interested in
photographing one bit, so Mam and I wandered off and
we met a group of people who had come to the Abbey
for a trip. There were six or seven in this group and they
came over to ask about me. They didn't speak much

English and Mam didn't speak much of their language, but soon Dad came over and he spoke to them. He told them all about me, an ex racing greyhound (levrier in their language) who had been abandoned in the countryside, but now had a home. They were upset to hear how I had just been left, though they laughed when they heard how I now had a luxurious life "en vacances dans un camping car, avec les saucisses et frites"! They couldn't get over how calm and gentle I was and how affectionate. All I could think was, "I know, I'm blinking marvellous!"

We went on a few trips from that campsite and once again, I went to places that I would not usually have been allowed into at home. I went into shops, chateaus and restaurants where, as usual, I was impeccably well-behaved. The day before we had to come home in the underground train we had to go into the town near the campsite. It was another very pretty town, where I had to wait outside the bakers whilst Dad went in to buy bread. We walked around the corner and came to a nice building with a ramp up to a sliding door. I thought at first it was a window, but as we got closer the glass slid sideways with a swishing sound. I got suspicious when we got inside as it smelled of cats, dogs and – yes, it was a vets! Apparently they even had them in foreign countries so you could go there during your holidays – how sneaky! The lady at the counter spoke to Dad in that strange language, and we had to sit and wait until the vet was free. Dad told me it was for my passport, I needed to be checked out by the vet, given a tablet, and then I could travel home with them the next day. The receptionist stood up and called us into the vet's room where she took the passport, checked it, and gave me a worming tablet (yes, the vet here was disguised as the receptionist – there was no limit to the sneakiness of these foreign vets). She stamped and signed the passport and said goodbye. That was that! I wished all trips to the vet were that easy and painless!

We had a last night at a campsite near "The Tunnel" as they called the train, and by the next afternoon we were off the train and travelling to one last campsite on our own side of the sea before we came home. I think this last campsite was my very favourite as it has rabbits – lots and lots of them. I walked round the site and not only could I smell them, but I could see them too. Dad said that my eyes were out on stalks most of the time around the walk (funny, but the rabbits in Ieper had not interested me at all). There was a fenced area on part of the site and here I had a chance to play with my ball, practising my returns. It was a great chance to have a stretch after being cooped up in the van for so long. I chuckled as I remembered that the first afternoon when we had been on the site in Normandy they had taken me to a quiet part of the site and thrown my ball for me. I had grabbed it on its bounce, and then sped off, disappearing around the corner behind some caravans and then back to them. Mam had gone white, as I am sure she thought that I was not going to come back, but I was better trained than she realised! At the end of the day, I knew where the sausages were. I had just needed that chance to stretch out and run in the lovely Normandy sunshine.

As Dad says, it's nice to travel and see new things, but I have to agree that it's even nicer to come home to your own bed. I think that I slept for a week when we got back – I was absolutely shattered. The weather had been beautiful all the time we were on holiday, but as soon as we got home it rained; Welcome to Wales!

The next year we went in The Tunnel, again but we went south and west to Normandy (that lovely site near the Abbey with the sausage and chips) and then down to the coast in Brittany. Here, I splashed in the sea and it was lovely. We even went into a very old part of the town and I shared a crepe with Dad; it was like a pancake, but thinner and with a lovely filling. However, by this time my demons had started; we were near some large vans that had sliding doors which sounded a bit like thunder when they were opened and closed, especially at night. I didn't like that and I started to worry. On a couple of occasions when I had asked to go out for my night-time wees, I had been reluctant to get back in the van and Dad had needed to lift me in. I had begun not to like it in the van at night.

Me measuring up a Chateau at Trevarez, Brittany (above) and on the beach at Concarneau (below)

10 - THE GREYT MIDSUMMER MARCH

I was incredibly lucky to have done my own bit in a fantastic, fund-raising event for Greyhound Rescue Wales. It all started when a few friends called around to the house with a plan to raise money for the charity. It was to be a sponsored walk from Brecon over the mountains and down the river Taff to Cardiff, along a path called The Taff Trail. This all meant nothing to me at that time, but Mam and Dad seemed suitably impressed. It was 55 miles in all, and it was decided that it could be done in three days. Dad said that we couldn't walk that far, but instead we would provide logistical support; in other words, we would provide food and drink and somewhere to rest along the route. Everyone agreed that this was a great idea, and that it would help make the walk much easier. After tracing the routes and the possible stops on the map, Dad agreed that we would check out these possible stopping points and then we would meet up in a few weeks with any other volunteers and we could show everyone the probable route.

The following weekend, we all jumped into the motorhome and drove to Brecon and then up over the hills and windy lanes all the way back down to Cardiff. I sat on the bench seats in the back of the van for most of the journey, but I did enjoy a nice walk along the side of a huge lake and then in a park once we got to Cardiff. I nearly winced on one bit where they drove into a narrow road of houses with parked cars outside and there was no room to turn the van around or even to go backwards – they just had to keep on going forwards. I think Dad was muttering a prayer as we squeezed through the gap which was so very narrow, but we did make it out the other end without scratching anything.

When the whole group met up in our house a few weeks later the volunteers and support team totalled nine walkers and three support plus me. As it was a long distance no greyhounds would be up to walking such a long way, but I would be the greyhound representative, albeit inside the motorhome. It was decided, though, that when the group got to Cardiff Bay at the end of the walk, people with greyhounds would meet up and we could all walk in together. The date for the walk was set for the 19th -21st June, around Midsummer's Day.

Dad and Mam showed everyone the planned stopping places, all on the Taff Trail or very near it. Dad even suggested that they would have a Greyhound Rescue Wales flag that they would put out of the van to show the walkers that they were nearby. Mam said that they would make loads of sandwiches, with a vegetarian option, and have water and drinks too. I would, of course, be available to provide greyhound hugs if required.

On the big day we didn't see them starting off from Brecon as we had to go to buy bread, water, and the major essential - cake. With the timetable we knew that they would be coming under the road at Llangynidr at a certain time, so we made our way to the bridge and waited – and there they came! There were still eleven of them – and a greyhound! Steve and Nan Horgan (GRW members from Cardiff) had brought their greyhound Raymond with them and on he trotted alongside them. I shook my head – will he still be that sprightly when we meet next up in the hills by the dam?

This was our first feed and rest stop; Mam and Dad pulled into the lay-by and opened up the roof and windows to cool the van (it was sunny for a change), and got out the folding table. They had prepared some food the day before – couscous with tomatoes, cashews with vegetable stock, and were now cutting, buttering and filling bread rolls. A car pulled up behind us – it was my Auntie Kerry (who I stayed with) with my friend Henry Henry! I went outside and stood with them as they talked to Dad. Then another car stopped - it was my Auntie Claire Price. Her husband Jonathan was one of the walkers. The cups of tea and coffee and cold drinks were ready and then Claire called out that the walkers were coming! We could see them walking up over the end of the dam and along the top towards us. I went with Dad to meet them and walked back with Auntie Sue who was another of the walkers. They looked tired but also so happy that they had made the first part of the walk. We stood around as they ate, drank and used the van toilet! Henry Henry and I greeted everyone. I had not met Raymond before, but we bumped noses and had a friendly sniff - he didn't even look tired!

Soon they were off again and we watched them go along the dam into the trees, tiny little human figures and one brown greyhound. Mam and Dad did a bit of washing up, then we put everything away and set off once more. For this stretch, the walkers had a very steep climb over the top of the hills and along a flat area until they dropped down into the next valley. We were to meet them on the flat area before it started to descend. It was a parking area where there had been trees but they had been cleared away so it was just a leafy dusty patch. As soon as they pulled up, before he had even put the gas on, Dad jumped out and put up the GRW flag (Dad had made this from a piece of dowel and had fastened a GRW tea-towel onto it – it looked Greyt!). Mam was cooking food and they cut more rolls ready for the hungry walkers. Dad even had time to take me for a little walk – we could hear a whistle in the distance rolling cross the lakes. He told me it was from a steam train on the far side of the reservoir – I could just make out the light sparkling on a shape that was puffing out clouds of grey smoke.

We sat in the sun whilst we waited for the walkers to arrive; it was such a lovely afternoon in a beautiful spot. I went back inside the van and sprawled on the settee as I was a bit sleepy. The next thing I remember was the van moving as Deb stepped inside. I smiled and went to the door to greet her. They had all arrived and, considering the climb, weren't too bad. Raymond was still quite sprightly, but Steve and Nan decided that it was now time for him to have a rest, so he climbed up with me and fell asleep on one of the settees.

This part of the walk was on the flat, maybe even with a slight descent. We had enough time to go to find our campsite for the night, and top up the water tanks before we went back to meet the walkers. Whilst waiting for them to come down past a church, Mam went to buy some chips and sausages from a chip shop we had just passed. As we waited, we shared them out – I even allowed Raymond to have some. The, by now, weary walkers emerged from the footpath beside the church and we met for one last time for that day. They were continuing into the town to a motel where they would eat and most of them were staying. We handed Raymond back and arranged to meet outside the motel the next morning.

I had a little walk around the campsite after our evening meal and couldn't wait for them to get the bed

out and let me sleep! It had been a tiring day helping
with the map-reading, the meeting and greeting and
ensuring that the welcome and catering were up to
scratch - Mam and Dad's had been the easy part. It was
still light when we drew down the shutters for the night
and it wasn't long before we were all asleep. I didn't
even wake in the night for wees.

I woke when Dad climbed off the bed to put the
kettle on. I lay there in a daze for a while, until my
cornflakes were ready and it was time for my first walk
of the day. Dad was dressed but had not washed and
shaved yet so he looked an absolute scruff-ball and I was
embarrassed to be seen out with him; I did my toilet as
fast as I could so I could get back into the van. They ate
hurriedly so we could set off quite early - we had to meet
the walkers at the first stop, but on the way we had to
collect their bags and packs from the motel they had
stayed at, and buy some food from a supermarket too.
The van was full of luggage and it was difficult even for
me to squeeze through – but I managed! Our first
meeting point was near the village where we had
narrowly slipped through the cars on our visit the month
before, but this time we had come up by a different
route. We parked on the corner of a road where the path

came right past us – we would see them coming from the front of the van. I waited by the kitchen as I knew that food would be prepared and, that if I was patient, the odd piece of ham or bread roll would come my way. It did too!

As Mam chopped and plated up the food, Dad put me on my lead and we walked down the track away from the van in the direction the walkers would be coming. Dad stopped to check his watch. A man on a bike headed towards us and Dad asked him whether he had seen a group of walkers and he replied that he had, only a few minutes behind. He rode away and within a couple of minutes we could hear voices then around the bend in the path the first of the group appeared – Jon and Jon! Dad cheered and they smiled back – for them it meant food and a break at last! Everyone gathered by the van and they took water, coffee, and ate some light food to keep them fuelled-up for the next part of the walk. It was good walking weather – a bit drizzly, but that appeared to help keep them all cool. I made my way between them to nuzzle up to everyone in turn, to remind them why they were walking – to help dogs like me who might have found themselves dumped in a field - or worse. I was also hoping to help with any food scraps, as I believe that recycling is a very important part of my job.

I stood with Mam and Dad and we watched them off again, one or two stopping to wave, just before disappearing round a clump of bushes and they were gone. Right – time now for us to clear the table; fold it away, paper cups and plates into a rubbish sack - on to the next stop.

This continued all day until our last stop where we met up with a group of other GRW supporters to await the walkers. I met Mr Ash for the first time, and his Mum and Dad, Gaynor and Nigel. He was a bit shy, but we did have a sniff and a tail wag. When the walkers appeared, most of them were limping and looked very uncomfortable; they had blisters from walking on the hard road surface in their boots. That was all of them, apart from Nan who was positively skipping - with no signs of any sore feet! Auntie Sue came back with us to the campsite as she was staying overnight in the bed over Mam and Dad's seats. That was until she saw the ladder, and it was decided that Dad would go up on top and Sue would share the settee with me instead. It was getting dark by the time we got back and ate food. Auntie Sue was complaining about her poor blistered feet and ended up sitting on the step of the van, dangling them into a bucket of soapy water! What the people in the other vans around us thought was another matter!

Bedtime - I had already jumped up on the bench seat before Sue and was falling asleep as she climbed under her sleeping bag. I was ok until she tried to roll over and pinned me against the back of the sofa; I growled. Sue apologised and gave me a bit more room, so I sighed and fell asleep again. This was repeated a few times in the night. How I wished that it was Dad here instead as he didn't fidget!

The walkers set out the next day from the point we had finished the night before. Here another group of supporters cheered and clapped as the brave travellers set out on what was their final and most important day – the walk from Tongwynlais to Cardiff Bay in front of the Welsh Assembly building. We jumped back into the van and made our way to the next stop, on the corner of a park on the edge of the city. It was a nice spot, not far from the river Taff. Dad took out the long pole from above the cab seats and used it to roll out the van awning and put up its legs, and Mam set out the table in its shade. The sun was shining and it was a gorgeous day. Steve Horgan's Dad arrived and sat in one of the chairs in the shade of the awning to wait for Steve and Nan to come walking in with the rest of them. Sally Howells, one of the GRW members who lived near Cardiff, also came to support the group. I went for a walk with Dad whilst Mam laid out the plates though I didn't want to go too far as I could smell the hot-dog sausages that were being warmed ready for the bread rolls. One of my very favourite things, those hot dog sausages.

We saw the walkers approaching and rushed back to the van to help lay the food out (I love helping with food - especially when it's hot dogs. Did I say they were one of my favourite things?). Mam had opened one of her jars of red onion chutney and was spooning it into the bread rolls – the smell of smoked sausage, fresh bread and tangy onions was absolutely amazing. I was very good and very helpy and I made sure that if there were any scraps of sausage or bread, I disposed of it in an ecologically friendly and responsible way - I ate them.

The walkers were tired and sore, but as this was

now the last stretch, they were also buoyed up with excitement. There was another stop before the very end of the walk at Cardiff Bay but it wasn't possible to get the van there so we were going to stay here, have something to eat ourselves after the walkers had left, then drive across the city to await the walkers at the end of the walk. It seemed like no time at all and they were setting off for the last stretch. They waved as they went and a couple of them were even singing!

We followed Dora the Sat Nav's directions to arrive at Cardiff Bay in plenty of time (Mam was very surprised that she had managed it). Dad had arranged to get the van into the Bay right in front of the big red building, which he told me was the Welsh Parliament. I was fairly impressed (well, that's what I told him).

There were loads and loads of people in the large bowl which was the entrance to the Bay. We parked the van and put out the Greyhound Rescue Wales flags. I was so pleased that GRW supporter Deb Williams and her lovely old hound, Lad, were there to greet us. I loved him – he was such a gent, a real gentlehound, who always said hello to me. He would kiss my nose and remind me of his name, and that he was, "getting on a bit, you know." Lad was wonderful. As we talked, a young boy came out from the crowd and over the square towards us; Dad was holding me on my lead and he smiled as the boy approached. "This is the famous Penny!" the boy said. Dad answered that indeed it was. I smiled and leant against the boy as he patted me. The boy said goodbye and wandered back into the crowds from which he'd come. Dad looked surprised – "He knew who you are!" he said to me. I just shrugged. As my publicist he, of all people, should have known how far my fame was spreading!

Mam walked me up the square away from the van and Dad followed with his camera. Apparently it was not long until all the walkers would arrive at the top end of the Bay. As I walked I spotted other greyhounds coming towards me, many familiar faces amongst them. They had arrived! I was beaming as I recognised those gallant humans who had given themselves sore feet, aching legs and blisters all for the benefit of rescued greyhounds like me. Mam and I joined them and accompanied them down towards the finishing point, which was on the very edge of the Bay itself. There were people gathered now to watch us in, supporters but also members of the public who just stopped and turned to see this crowd of greys and humans marching together. Mam handed me to Auntie Sue, who walked me the last bit of the way. There were loud cheers and applause as we made it to the end. I beamed with pride as the walkers joined together and a man with a beard made a speech along with Alain Thomas, the founder of Greyhound Rescue Wales. The man with the beard was Boyd Clack, a great supporter or our cause and one of the Patrons of the charity. He gave me a cuddle at the end of the walk, even though I tried to explain that I was merely one of the Support Team. I was so pleased that me, Mam and Dad had done our bit!

All in all, it had been a terrific adventure; I was in awe of the humans who had walked all the way from Brecon to Cardiff for us hounds. 55 miles. Dad said that it raised £7,000 for the charity, which even to a greyhound was an incredible sum of money; just think how much good that could do. Or how many bacon rolls it could buy…

The heroic marchers were;

Jonathan Price

Jonathan Baker

Deb Williams

Rich Nokes

Debra Allen

Sue Lewis

Emyr Evans

Gary Lewis

Steve Horgan

Nan Horgan

Amanda Aston

Raymond Horgan

Support Crew

Claire Price

Armelle Dignam

Chris Dignam

Tilly Price

Penny Dignam

The Support Team - Me and Mam (Mrs Crafty Dog) at the end of the Greyt Midsummer March

10 - MY DEMONS

The mind is a complex thing- for everybody - whether they are human or dog. Some things I have control over but others are just beyond me. I'd always been sensitive, as most greyhounds are – I've been no different really to my brothers and sisters, my kennel mates or my later friends. I've told you all about my concern that I was going to be abandoned again, and I think that was what really damaged my confidence. I was left out on my own in that field for so long, with dark nights, strange sounds, invisible animals and insects that nibbled at me in the shadows, lonely cold and wet. I think my spirit was at its lowest ebb and I was so happy to be rescued by Mr Jones and Twm, then Sarah and finally my Dad and Mam. I have never been as happy as I am now when I lie with them, in my own forever home; belonging to my own pack, feeling loved. But, somehow, at the back of my mind, I still have the niggling fear that this is only a passing thing and that it could all end at any time and I would be dumped again - in the cold, wet and dark.

I had only been with Dad and Mam for a few weeks when they had taken me out one evening for our 7 o'clock daily visit to Nana in the Nursing Home. It was dark, but that was ok, as they were with me. I could hear noises – bangs and cracks – in the distance but nothing to scare me, and I could see flashes of light but they too didn't bother me. We arrived at the Home and I stood to get out. Dad opened the tailgate, clipped my lead on and I jumped down. There were more loud bangs but they weren't close by and I felt that I had nothing to worry about, as Dad took me up the slope to the door of the Home where my Nana lived. He pressed the button on the door and we waited for someone to answer. Almost immediately, there was a deafening screeching sound, a flash of bright light and an enormous explosion not more than twenty feet above my head. We all jumped, even the humans, but I think I jumped higher. The door opened and I ran inside, dragging Dad behind me. I was absolutely terrified. What was that? What was happening? The flash and the screeching – what terrible noises! I didn't know what to do – all I could think was that I needed a safe place to hide away from any more of these noises. I don't remember getting to Nana's room, all I wanted to do was hide. I flew past Nana and went to the corner of the room where there were thick curtains I could snuggle in. I could feel my body shaking; my heart was thumping, I was panting heavily and in a blind panic. The sounds outside kept on and, though they were further away now, to me every pop or crack felt as if my head or my heart was going to explode. I lay there shaking for a while but eventually I calmed down and came out. If Dad cuddled me I found myself starting to shake again. I couldn't understand that – it was as if my mind and my body were outside my control.

For the next few weeks there was still the occasional loud bang that made me scared, if only briefly. Though Dad and Mam both tried to calm me down it wouldn't work; my mind went back to that first huge explosion and I feared that one of those would soon follow and make me shake with terror. The anticipation of that loud bang happening in turn made me fearful.

It was a very wet winter that year, but I coped, as long as there were no loud bangs. When spring approached we went through an even wetter phase in the weather. One afternoon the sky grew very dark, and I could feel the pressure change – it was increasing, making my ears throb and I could feel the air almost crackle. Mam was home with me and she didn't appear to be worried about the pressure change. All of a sudden there was a bright flash of light and an enormous rumbling sound that shook the whole house, followed by a loud bang. I jumped and I'm sure that my heart tried to leap out of my chest. I didn't know what to do – I was so frightened but literally had nowhere to run to. Mam came to me but I didn't want to be cuddled or held. I knew that the chair in the living room had a small space behind it and so I went in there. It had walls on two sides, the tall Scots cupboard on another and the back of Dad's chair at the front, with a gap large enough for me to get through. Somehow, my mind reasoned in my terror that this would be a safe space. Mam took a blanket and stretched it over the top from the Scots cupboard to the chair so it formed a roof and I felt that I was protected. It took me back in my mind to the flimsy but sheltering bit of tin roof I had in the ruined barn in that field when I had been dumped. It made me feel a bit more secure and I settled there in the semi dark. I lay there panting and shaking, listening now to the heavy rain that had followed the peel of thunder. The storm passed over us as suddenly as it had started and as soon as I calmed down I felt so very tired that I fell asleep.

Over the next few months we must have had ten or more storms, some just one peel of thunder but others lasting a few hours. Mam and Dad kept the cover over this area and it became my safe place, "cwtsh" they called it, the Welsh word for a cuddle, or place you put precious things for safe keeping. I now had a bed here too so that whenever I felt worried or insecure, I'd go here. Often I would feel the air pressure change, or hear a loud sound too far away for them to hear, but I would hear it. I'd get up from wherever I was in the house and head straight for my cwtsh. They said that I was their precious girl, that went to their cwtsh to be safe and secure.

When we were next at the vet, Mam asked about something to calm my nerves and I was given some tablets. Their big concern was fireworks season, the weeks leading up to and after "Guy Fawkes". I don't know who this person is, or was, but I would love to thank them for the terror they instil in so many dogs and other animals too – even lots of humans who hate the loud bangs. The tablets made me drowsy so that I would be half asleep when the bangs started. They tried them during a thunderstorm, but I was still frightened though unable to move (or think) properly.

The great fear got a lot worse after one particular trip in the motorhome; we were at a craft fair in Brecon and staying on a campsite not far from the town. I had no worries or fears of being in the van – it was after we'd been on those lovely holidays to Brugge and Normandy. We arrived in the early evening, had eaten and then had a lovely walk in the warm summer sunshine down the hill to the river and back up again. We'd stayed at this site once before, and I really liked it here because it was quiet, had lots of interesting things to sniff and explore and nice walks. As I lay on my settee after our meal, I felt the air begin to tingle and the pressure increase. I started to pant as I knew what would soon follow; there was a huge peel of thunder that shook the motorhome. I flew off the settee and shot for the door – I needed to get out. Dad clipped my lead on and we jumped down into the rain. I was so frightened that I couldn't hold my bladder, so I weed outside the van and then refused to get back in. Dad lifted me up into the van and I headed up the back to the seats. I jumped on the settee towards the corner and huddled in it as tightly as I could. The rain was now hammering down, like a thousand dogs were jumping up and down on the roof. This time Dad had some calming drops which he put in my mouth. They helped me a little, and as the rain subsided, so did my fear and, again, I fell asleep - totally exhausted.

That would have been it, but we stayed on the site the next evening and just after tea, we had an almost identical storm. This time the heavy rain came first and the thunder lasted longer. The whole van shook with every crash of thunder and this time the calming drops didn't work at all – I was almost swigging them from the bottle – "So much for herbal remedies," I heard Dad say. That was why I began to get wary of the motorhome – this was just a month before we went to Brittany where I heard those rumbling van doors. Even though I had been on so many lovely day trips and holidays in the van, I started to dislike it. My stupid mind made me begin to think that a drip of rain would mean heavy rain, which would mean thunder – which would mean me being terrified. I grew to hate the rain. I grew to fear the rain. I began to fear our van.

This all came to a head when we went to visit Mam's Auntie Molly in Lincolnshire. The journey up to our first overnight at Kenilworth had been ok and we had even had a visit from Mam's friends. I had enjoyed being fussed by them so much as they talked all evening. However, after they left, and it got dark I heard tapping on the roof – I stiffened - the first drips of rain? Dad told me not to worry as it was just leaves falling from a tree overhead, but no matter what he said, my mind knew better – it was rain which meant thunder. I stared at the roof, worried, asked to go out, had to be lifted back inside, worried some more then eventually fell asleep.

Up at Lincoln, we stayed on a small campsite next to a large grassy field where Dad walked me. It was nice. We visited a couple of stately homes and I'd walked around their parkland and had even eaten outside at their coffee shops. I enjoyed meeting Auntie Molly – she was very kind and lovely - but that Sunday evening back at the campsite wasn't an easy one for me; it wasn't raining but there was the occasional tap on the roof – that sound of falling leaves. However, there were strange noises that I couldn't quite hear but I could sense; they woke me up when I slept and troubled me during the day. Then there was the sound of engines roaring – jet planes taking off and landing not far away which went on all night. By Monday afternoon I'd stopped eating – my appetite was gone as I worried about the strange sounds in my head and the tap tap of rain on the roof. By the next morning I still wasn't eating, so Dad went to see the site owner to pay her, and we left for home; it was a really long journey – 6 hours I think it took – but I was totally frazzled and my head couldn't take it any more. I wanted home, my own bed and safety. Apparently, we were between three large air bases and planes were taking off to drop bombs on another country far away. As for the strange sounds in my head, the lady on the site said that it might have been ultrasound emitted by radar and sonar at the air bases, and that even her TV remote was not working. All I know is that it nearly sent me mad.

Once home I ate like a horse! I went to see the vet and was checked out but was given a clean bill of health. I was physically fit, but how could I explain that I was a nervous wreck – the result of being a worrier with a profound fear of abandonment. I can't help it – it's the baggage I carry. I consider that I am fortunate to have an understanding family that are willing to work with me, even if it means cancelling their holiday and travelling across the country to get me back to where I feel safe and secure – our home.

Within a week of getting back, Dad spoke to a behaviourist working for Greyhound Rescue Wales who came around to see me (one of my friends had referred to her as a "shrink" whatever that meant). By this stage, even the sound of rain hitting the window in the house was making me fret. The behaviourist spoke to me and to Dad and Mam too, and made some suggestions, things to try and things to mention to the vet. Apparently, because I was good at obedience, and was a show–off and a quick learner, she thought that some of the distraction techniques would work.

I went to the vet the next week and Dad explained about the distraction therapy, as well as the need for something to take the edge off my worry, something similar to the tablets humans take for anxiety. I was given some tablets, to be used when I was having one of my severe bouts of anxiety, such as thunder or fireworks. They work in a way that helps prevent the fear settling and leaving a memory. Let's be honest, we were prepared to try anything.

The distraction therapy I really like; it involves Mam keeping a large bowl of treats on the coffee table by her side, then if I look concerned by, say, glancing at the window, she gives me a treat. The sound that once frightened me will, over time, become one that means a treat - a positive. I have to admit that I was sceptical at first, but it does seem to work. It has taken a couple of years but I am getting better and can even tolerate some degree of rain before I start to worry and I don't worry as much now. It's not a miracle cure, but it helps. (I even learnt that if I looked at the window I got a reward so I used to try that one now and again for a treat!)

Then there's The Moody Blues. I've always loved music (though I don't like the sound of live music on the hi-fi - the clapping and cheering unnerves me) and whenever they leave me in the house (to go shopping, for example) they leave the radio on. During one of my nervous days, when it was raining heavily, I was beginning to look worried and I started to pant. Dad went to the music machine and searched out a CD, which he put on. I was still panting and lay in my cwtsh and was going to shake when I heard the music starting. I don't know what it was, but the sound was strangely compelling to me and I just had to listen to it. As I did so, I found myself unwinding. I could still hear the heavy rain but the music was so - enchanting I suppose - that it drew me in. Dad was as amazed as I was. He called Mam over and showed her what was happening and she too was surprised.

Really loud bangs like thunder or fireworks are another matter; the new tablets relieve my anxiety and help me relax; whereas before I would be terrified, panting and drooling and was once even sick, this is nowhere near as bad. I know that I couldn't face a proper fireworks display – that would just be too much. They have a huge display on the pitch behind our house and I have to go to dog-sitters when that is on, usually for the few days before and after Guy Fawkes. Where I go there are fireworks though not so close, and there are always lots of other greyhounds there to help distract me. I, and my family, know my limitations.

I still love going out in the van during the day, and love my road trips, but I can't face overnights yet. This is going to take some more confidence building. I am happy to go anywhere in the motorhome and I love Dinefwr Park and I hope to do some short trips away, but I know that I will never be able to take trips through the tunnel again. That would be a bit too much pressure.

A couple of month's back we all went in the van down to Devon where we visited a large park with an enormous house in it called Knightshayes. We walked round the parkland, and I had a huge ice-cream. That evening we stayed on a little camp-site alongside a lovely river walk which we did as the sun was setting. Across the river there were loads of rabbits which Dad had to point out to me. When we got back I was so tired that I could hardly wait for the bed to come out and I could sleep. I think they must have slipped me a tablet as I was not at all bothered as it grew dark. They kept the small light and music on until quite late but we were all so shattered after what had been a really enjoyable day that we slept like logs, the three of us. It helped that there was no rain but we are all hoping that we can do a few more one night trips and rebuild my confidence again.

I'm not the only greyhound or even dog to be scared of loud noises or rain; I have many friends who have the same problems too. I can remember some years ago going up to the greyhound sanctuary at Hillcrest and spending Guy Fawkes Night and even New Year with friends. There were fewer fireworks here than at home and they were much further away but there were still enough to scare me. I remember having one of my tablets and then going to find a quiet place to hide, usually with my friend Gabe. He was a big greyhound boy who was even more scared of loud bangs than I was, and we would cuddle up on Sandra the Sanctuary Manager's bed and shake quietly together until we fell asleep.

I realise that sometimes Mam and Dad have to go away and that I can't go with them as I can't face overnights in the van. So, Mam and Dad let me stay with my friends at their houses. I stay with my Auntie Kerry and Uncle Mike sometimes, where my friends Popsy, Henry Henry and Mr D'Arcy live (remember I mentioned earlier that Popsy and Henry Henry have gone over the rainbow bridge now). I love staying there as they spoil me. On one of my stays me, HH and Popsy went out for last wees and after our toileting the others went back in the house but I wandered behind their shed as there was a very sniffable smell there. When I went to turn around I couldn't – there was a wall on one side and the shed on the other and a wall in front of me. I was stuck facing down the gap towards the wall. Auntie Kerry came out with a torch to find me stuck behind the shed. She tried calling me to turn round but I couldn't. By now we were both beginning to panic a bit, and I heard Auntie Kerry saying that she might have to get Mike to take the shed down! Then she just shouted "Back, back". I remembered that Dad had taught me to do this in the utility room when there was no room to turn. So I stepped backwards. She said it again, so I did it again. She called me a clever girl, and we did it again until I was out of the gap. That was an adventure! I love going to Auntie Kerry's as they have beef mince in the week, on Tuesdays its "Sossidge Tuesday" which means all us dogs get sausages for tea - and I can sleep wherever I like!

I also stay with Uncle Colin and my Auntie Trish; they have lots of dogs staying in their house for their holidays, and I have made many friends through staying with them. One evening I was sitting on the floor and the other dogs were sharing a settee, with Colin and Trish on the other one. I stood up and barked at Uncle Col who got up as he thought I might need the loo. He fell for it – as soon as he stepped away from the settee I jumped on and cuddled up next to Auntie Trish! Col had to sit on the floor in front of me. He was very kind to give up his seat on the settee for me. What a gent! Uncle Col and Auntie Trish call in to collect me and to bring me back and I must admit I do get excited when they arrive as I know that I will be having a great time on my holidays with them. I do miss my Mam and Dad, but I prefer staying with Kerry and Mike or Colin and Trish as I worry in the van overnight.

I must also mention my other great friends who visit me quite often; Lolly and Lulu. They are probably my best greyhound friends, though sometimes Lulu can be a bit grumpy. Lolly always wants me to play with her all the time, but I am getting a bit long in my five teeth now and just turn my back on her and wander off, with her following me, sighing. I go and stay with them and they sometimes stay here in my house, usually when their Mum (my Auntie Pam) is shopping or visiting someone, and their Dad (my Uncle Dave) is working. I love going to stay with them as their garden is huuuuuge! And there is some really great long grass that I like to try and chew, though never with much success as I don't have any molars any more and just dribble and foam. Dad says I look like I have rabies. Whatever.

Above - Belton House – the day before my melt-down and below, relaxing at Auntie Pam and Uncle Dave's

10 - BECOMING THE CRAFTY DOG

Dad and I have been scratching our heads trying to remember how and when I became 'The Crafty Dog'. That's a long time ago (for a greyhound it's even longer than for a human). I think it began just after I came to live here with my new Mam and Dad. They were always busy in the kitchen cooking and chopping, putting stuff in bottles, or else painting and drawing. They cooked loads of fruit and vegetables, and put these mixtures in glass bottles and I wondered what they did with all this food – jars and jars and jars of it – where did it all go?

One Saturday morning (I knew it was Saturday as it was a day that Dad had not gone to "The Office") plastic boxes were being filled and carried out to the car. At the same time, my coat and lead were both brought off their hook and I was taken out to the car too. The space behind their seats and in front of mine was piled high with boxes and crates (I couldn't believe how much they could get in the car).

We left home, but were soon pulling up outside a building along with many other cars. I watched their crates and boxes leave the car one-by-one, or two-by-two, until there was only me left. I sat around for a while until I heard the door locks click, the hatch opened and Dad leaned in to clip on my lead. "Come on Penny," he said, "Time for you to do some work!"

My heart sank at first as I had visions of being back at the track, but I couldn't have been more wrong if I'd tried. We went inside a large room where there were lots of tables set out in rows, and behind each one stood a person or maybe two. The tables were laden with pictures, cakes, clothes, more cakes, bread, cheese, toys, even more cakes, jewellery, jams, glassware and cakes. Mam stood behind their own table full of those jars and glasses; brightly coloured glasses, the ones they had painted at home, and the jars full of the fruit and vegetables they had cooked. At the front of the table were small opened jars of food, with crackers and spoons so people could taste it. I could smell strawberry, raspberry, garlic, and onion - all the things I knew they cooked. Dad took me behind their table and I stood beside him as people started to come over. They spoke to Dad and Mam, tasted some of the little jars that had been opened specially (by putting spoons of their food, apparently called jams or chutneys, onto crackers), then they gave us money in exchange for the jars of food or for the painted glasses. Now I must admit that seemed a much better way of using money than betting on us racing dogs. I smiled.

And that's where the first person asked, "Is that The Crafty Dog?" pointing to me. I grinned back and I heard Mam laugh, "Yes, this is Penny the Crafty Dog!"

I met loads of people who wanted to know my story, so Dad explained about my ex-racing days. Some people brought me pieces of cake, and bacon, and part of a sausage roll. I decided that this was the type of job I wanted – forget running round a track, bring me the friendly people with the bacon rolls!

A lady came over to us and pointed at the banner on the front of their stall, on which was a picture of a greyhound wearing a hat; she asked Dad, "Why are you called 'Crafty Dog'?"

Dad explained about our long involvement with greyhound rescue. We had started as fund raisers, and that this had now grown into our own craft business - making jams and chutneys, incredible hand-painted glassware, and spreading the word about how wonderful greyhounds were. Crafts that had begun all because of the greyhounds, so the name they had settled on was "Crafty Dog". I went round the table and the lady fussed me as she talked to Dad about me. The lady said that I was gorgeous, and that she hadn't realised how quiet and gentle greyhounds were - or how beautiful. And she bought some jam.

This work was called "going to Craft Fairs" and it was what we did most weekends (and still do today). I have been to fairs across Wales and even into England. One of the best was the one where the people dress up in funny clothes – top hats and the women wear tight clothes called corsets (apparently they are Steam Punks). That's where I met my Auntie Charlotte; she's lovely and always calls me Pen Pen. Her fairs are usually bursting with people and most of them know who I am!

People come from far and wide to buy the jams and chutneys Mam and Dad make. I don't always go with them as some places don't let dogs in. Pfft! They don't realise how famous I am. People often come to the house, where I am always pleased to greet them. It's my role as The Crafty Dog to welcome people to the house and keep them entertained whilst Mam or Dad gets the jams or glassware for them.

They even sell their jams and glassware from people's shops, which means that we often go on road trips to them to deliver our crates of jam or glassware (and books too). I love this as at some of these shops I am even allowed inside. There's a lovely tea room in the hills near Merthyr where I go in and sit on my bed next to Mam and Dad and they bring me ham, a bowl of milk and I even get to share some of Dad's scones with (our) jam and clotted cream. Auntie Lynda who runs the "Old Barn Tea Rooms" always makes a big fuss of me - I love being a celebrity! I am given my very own bowl of milk, mind, and huge handfuls of ham. I think I love going there best of all.

As I said before, Mam and Dad had had greyhounds for many years and people would often ask them questions about them. They had also fostered dogs, which they spoke to me about. Dad had written a few pieces about these dogs in some magazines, but people would often come up to him at talks and craft fairs and ask when he was going to write a book. He just laughed – "No time," he replied. What Mam and I didn't know was that he was quietly writing something he thought he would put out as an "electronic book". He finished it and put it on Amazon. That was that, or so we thought.

This first book that Dad wrote was about all the greyhounds that had lived in our house before me; it all began with Sally, the big white greyhound (I still wear the collar Nana bought her for Christmas many years ago) and of course Sammy, the black dog that watches over us. Up until a year ago, Dad used to go to out to work every day, and come home (tired and miserable, Mam said) in the evening just after tea-time. One day he came home at lunchtime instead, and a lady arrived not long afterwards with a camera and Mam, Dad and me had our picture taken in the garden, and in the living room with Dad's laptop (which had a picture of the electronic book on). A few days later the newspaper came out, and the picture of me and Dad and Mam was in it; it said about how he had written the book and that it was available on computers around the world. The story in the paper was about the book and about me and the sad life of many ex-racing dogs.

When Dad came home from work the next day he said that our local library in Clydach had asked for us to go and talk about the book and rescued greyhounds. A few weeks later, we all trotted round to the library, and I met more of my public who had come to see me and listen to Dad talk about me and their other dogs. At this particular talk people were a bit disappointed, as some of them wanted to buy a "proper" copy of the book, not just a computer one (something they said was "virtual" which I didn't quite understand). I guessed that they just wanted a signed photo of me! Liz at the library happened to mention in passing that there was a man who lived nearby who published books, so a week later we met the lovely gentleman who called himself "Wuggs". He persuaded Dad to print and publish the book himself, so a few months later (after Dad had spent many evenings typing away in the room upstairs) a pile of boxes arrived – Sally and Sammy's stories were available for everyone to read on paper!

That's when things took off – book orders came in from around the world and we started going out and giving talks about the life of rescued greyhounds in loads of places across the country. The crowds ranged from a dozen (rarely) to over a hundred (on a number of occasions). People all wanted to hear about the life of ex-racing greyhounds but more importantly, they wanted to meet one – and that was superstar ex-athlete me! I like to greet the people, as I am such a sociable character, so when Dad talks I like to work my audience, going along the rows to say hello to everyone in turn. At many of the talks people tell me that they or their parents used to have greyhounds and race them. Dad is always at pains to point out that it's only a minority of people in the industry that mistreat their dogs, but that minority gives the rest of them a bad name. I was never mistreated, just never loved (Sally and Sammy on the other hand had both been beaten); I was just left to fend for myself in that farmer's field.

I am always aware that I'm an ambassador for my breed, a role that I take very seriously. I'm always well-behaved, friendly and willing to give everyone a cuddle. We are always surprised when people say that they have never ever met a greyhound, so I want their first impression to be a positive one. I am always grateful to the rescue organisation that found me a home, so wherever we go we always take the Greyhound Rescue Wales collection pot and leaflets. I know that we have had greyhounds rehomed after a number of our talks, so I can hold my head up and say that due to my wonderful temperament (and modesty) I have helped my fellow hounds.

I have even been asked to help people with stress (though Dad has said that I have caused him more stress and worry than the other dogs! Hah!). Greyhound Rescue Wales heard about a scheme to help students at the local university who were finding that exams and college life was making them anxious. The idea was to take a group of chilled-out dogs to meet them (in small groups) so the students could cuddle and fuss us and this would help them to unwind. You won't find a more relaxed and laid-back dog than a greyhound, and I love cuddles and fusses. We met the other dogs in the car park and then went into the college building where we waited in a large room for the students to come inside. They came in about five or six at a time and for 20 minutes they all sat amongst us as we hounds wandered between them being cuddled and loved. The students enjoyed it - as did we too; some of them had dogs of their own who they were missing, and a few actually had greyhounds or lurchers. Dad said that he wished they had been able to do this when he had been a student at this university but I guess that was a very long time ago in less enlightened times! We were there for an hour or so, and there was even a film crew who recorded us for television. Yes, I was on Welsh TV the very next day!

When I was walking round the students, having cuddles, and they were talking to me I remembered when I used to go to see Nana in her home with the old people and Mam would take me round the big room where they would all sit to watch the tellybox or eat. They would reach out and stroke me, and talk to me. I loved that too - I never had grandparents of my own, apart from my Nana so the people in the home in a way became a part of my family. I loved going round to see them. The nurses were always taken aback when particular residents would talk to me and tell me about their own dogs, maybe even when they were children themselves. What surprised the nurses was that some of these residents hadn't spoken for ages but seeing and touching me had brought them out of themselves, if only for a few minutes. Dad said it was because greyhounds had old souls and were magical. Maybe there's something in that, Dad.

It's a strange thing about us greyhounds that we enjoy the company of our own breed. When we grow up we are raised in groups of greyhounds - always trained together and raced together. It's natural that we recognise the greyhound-shape, and that includes our smaller cousins, whippets and even the tiny Italian greyhounds (or Iggy's). Many crossed greyhounds (these are called Lurchers) have the family shape and manners. Just seeing that shape trotting towards you makes me smile and get excited. I am not bothered about cats (though I know most hounds aren't the same!) and I can tell the difference between small dogs and cats. I am a little unsure about some small dogs and puppies, as they tend to jump in my face and scare me a bit. I always give them a warning growl if they jump up, then I step back, but if they persist, they'll get a snap. I very rarely get to that stage!

I can be a bit cheeky, Dad tells me. I just think I can be assertive. When they work at the fair at Talgarth near Brecon I stay with my Auntie Sara, one of our GRW friends who lives nearby. I have known her for ages and I love her very much (and I know that she loves me too!). She lives with her gentle old greyhound called Barney. I smile when I think about how I barge in and take over and old Barney just sighs and takes himself off to the other room as I climb on the settee next to Sara or her Dad (who is my unofficial Gramps). I never had a Gramps of my own, so I borrow Sara's Dad who loves to see me when I visit. Barney is very patient, though I have heard him muttering about me being a "bloody Diva" as he wanders off. I just shrug and go to find whatever's left in his food bowl.

We sometimes go up to the Greyhound Sanctuary at Hillcrest which is not far from us. Here, we drop off bedding, toys, and food for the dogs that are there awaiting homes of their own. We used to have summer fairs up here and I can remember my very first one. It was a very busy day, and we were staffing our Crafty Dog stall, which was doing very well. Afterwards, some of us stayed behind for our people to have something to eat and drink. Dad was sitting on one of the big settees in the conservatory and I climbed up next to him. I cuddled up, and started to go off to sleep. The next thing I knew, another big dog had climbed on the other side and was also trying to have fusses with Dad. I was a bit tired and grouchy (as I recall, which is unlike me) and I found myself growling at that other dog, who looked a bit taken aback and climbed off the settee. I laugh now as I realise it was my good friend Caine who lives with Uncle Colin and Auntie Trish! I must repeat that it was not like me – my only excuse was that I was very, very tired. In fairness, Caine doesn't bear a grudge and has never growled at me when I sit on his settee next to Uncle Colin when I go there on my holidays!

All that takes me back to the times we have been to greyhound events with the jams and chutneys and glasses, or the book readings. I especially enjoy meeting the gang at the greyhound walks we have around here. I meet some of my friends that I haven't seen for a while. When Dad had his last book-launch Snip and Freda came with Uncle Alain, Matty and Darcy came along with Auntie Dianne and Mr D'Arcy with me Auntie Kerry and Uncle Mike. I often enjoy the meeting and greeting more than the walk and after a hundred metres I turn around and go back to the van or car. I am getting a bit older and creakier now so long walks in damp weather are less appealing.

I think I'll end by going back to the beginning, if you see what I mean; it really explains about me and The Crafty Dog. Remember that lady I mentioned that came over to us at my first Craft Fair and pointed at the banner on the front of their stall, on which was a picture of a greyhound wearing a hat; the lady that asked Dad, "Why are you called 'Crafty Dog'?"

This is the rest of their conversation. Dad told her, "We've been involved with greyhound rescue for 15 years or so. When we started off we fund raised for greyhound charities. The charity we were involved with folded when Swansea Dog Track closed but we still wanted to meet people, explain about rescued greyhounds and contribute to charities. We started coming to craft fairs, but needed a name. We hit upon Crafty Dog as we make crafts, and started because of the greyhounds – so our logo is a greyhound in an artist's beret. The 'Cymru' was added because there's a Crafty Dog in the USA."

"So your money all goes to the greyhounds?" she asked.

"No", Dad explained, "It's our own business now, but we do still help to raise funds, and we help publicise the plight of ex-racing greyhounds and those that often never made it to the track." With that he put his hand on my shoulder and cuddled me.

"Is she friendly?" the lady asked.

I walked round the table and gently stepped towards her, lowering my head slightly as she reached out her hand. The lady stroked my head.

"Her coat is so smooth – it's like silk!"

I looked up at her and beamed, and gave her a toothy smile (I still had a mouthful of lovely almost white teeth then).

"What's her name?" the lady asked.

"This is our beautiful Penny," Dad said. I looked at him as he mentioned my name.

"How beautiful," the lady breathed, looking into my lovely deep brown eyes. "What's her story?"

"It's a long one," he said, "And it all started the day we found a Penny…"

Me and Mam working hard at a Craft Fair, and below, me and Dad proving that greyhounds can do obedience.

10 - A DAY IN THE LIFE OF A CRAFTY DOG

I have often been asked what I do all day apart from look gorgeous; well, this is the typical day in the life of a Crafty Dog; I wake between 6 and 7 o'clock, depending on the amount of sunshine streaming through the windows on the settee in the living room. If I have not got up, I lie in my bed or on my settee to wait for Dad to come in and I wave my paw at him to have a fuss and maybe a quick cuddle. (I love the magic paw – whenever they stop fussing me, or just wander past and I consider that I have not had enough attention I wave my front paw, in a most imperious way, apparently). If I have woken up and need the loo, I stretch off the settee, have a huge shake, then wander to the foot of the stairs and give out a gentle squeak or a whine. I don't usually need to bark. That brings Dad downstairs (very rarely is it Mam!). Next it's either toilet and food or food then toilet, depending on my particular needs at that moment. My breakfast of choice is porridge, milk and a little ham (with my bladder tablets in it – old age doesn't come alone!). I usually then follow Dad back upstairs with his coffee and Mam's tea, and I lie on the bed with them for a while 'til they go down back for their breakfast.

If they are going out, they go back upstairs and get dressed for out, or if not, dressed for the house. This is where I have to read the room and what they are doing; if there are crates and bags of glass and jams in the car it could mean a show, in which case I might go with them, or may stay home. Either way, I now have to follow Dad round the house so he doesn't forget me. If the harness comes out, I know it's out in the car. If not, then I know that either Bluey will be filled up with treats or I will get a bacon sizzler – either way it's a win for me!

If I stay home, I usually play with Bluey for a while, rolling it around the floor until I get tired (or food stops falling out) and then I climb up on the settee for a sleep. They usually leave the radio on for me. I like the music and the sound of the people talking helps me feel relaxed too. When they get home I am usually still asleep, but if I hear the car pulling up I jump down, and run to the door to greet them. They usually come in through the kitchen door, but sometimes they surprise me by coming in through the front door and I have to run back through the room to them! Sneaky.

When I was younger, I went out for a walk after my breakfast and when I got back I sat back in my bed to catch my breath and just enjoy being there – in a real home of my own. In those days, Dad would go out to "work" and leave me with a small handful of treats which I would eat within a few minutes. By the time I'd finished them Mam would be downstairs and making her breakfast cereal, where once again I would have a small taster. This has changed since Dad only goes as far as his office upstairs; now I might follow him upstairs or just sun puddle in one of my beds in the living room.

If it's a home day, I might go upstairs to the big bed and just sun puddle there until its lunchtime. I know when it's 12 o'clock and time for dinner – my body clock has an unerring accuracy! I trot down and find Mam wherever she is and remind her that I need feeding or I could just pass out with hunger or even go dead. My favourite lunch is a deconstructed sardine sandwich –

that is, chopped up bread mixed with a tin of sardines (in tomato sauce if I'm lucky) and some water. If Dad makes this I also get some chopped up fresh baby tomatoes too. They sometimes try and slip my arthritis tablets in this, but I'm usually clever enough to sniff them out and leave them well alone!

If I have gone back up to bed for a nap for an hour after my lunch, I know there's a good chance (if I time it correctly) that Mam will be finishing her own crusts and will be putting them in my food bowl. If I come down and crusts are not forthcoming (as she has not eaten yet) then I might have to remind her by giving her a nudge with my nose, or if that fails, I might need to bark (she gets very involved in her glass painting at the table and forgets to eat). I have to prepare myself for this by a long stretch and a good gulp of air, and then a rumbling as I clear my throat and finish with a nice sharp bark. I have taught them to understand that this means, "Excuse me – it's food time."

After my lunch it's a toilet stop, then I go back up to the big bed and sleep until 4-ish. When I go back down I ask for my tea, and keep asking every 15 minutes until they eventually weaken and they start preparing my meal. This is usually kibble with some soft dog food or their food (from their own tea, or leftovers from lunchtime or the evening before). This can be pasta, or rice, cooked vegetables, or fish, or cooked eggs. This is good for me, as with my lack of teeth I can't eat hard things, so things have to be soft or chopped up small. My favourite food is pasta with something; either smoked salmon and peas, or cooked tomatoes and bacon. This is always when the arthritis tablets get past me!

After our tea, we watch TV together, and I try and get them to sit with me on the settee. If that doesn't work I go to my "cwtsh" or bed behind Dad's chair. This is my special safe place and I feel secure there, but it's a nice place to sleep anyway. As soon as my meal is eaten, I wait in the living room and I look back at them, hinting very heavily that they should come in with me. As soon as they are finished, in they come and I sit by Dad's chair. I try and get him to sit with me sometimes by nudging him and walking towards the settee. When he understands, I will wait for him to sit next to Mam then curl up next to him. My favourite part of the day, all of us together, watching TV. Wonderful. There's nothing like being part of a pack and all being together.

Sometimes in the afternoon I might decide that I need a walk. This is quite a recent thing that Mam has got me into as I am not really interested in walks around here. I love a trot around the cricket field behind our house and if I am so inclined I might even chase my ball and bring it back after Dad or Mam have thrown it. It's great exercise for me and they seem to get a real "buzz" from watching me do it. All part of the service!

I used to get a bad tummy if I was empty too long overnight. This was solved by me having a small bowl of cereal for supper after nine o'clock. I love multigrain hoops with water and milk. It's just enough to stop my tummy rumbling in the night. I sleep on the settee at night and only occasionally have to call Dad to come down and let me out for the toilet.

Well, that's not strictly true; in the dark months when the rain and fireworks start I find it more comfortable downstairs in my cwtsh behind the chair. I feel safe there. If it's noisy, with the rain hammering on the windows, I sleep in my kitchen bed curled up tight. This is where Sammy and Sally used to sleep and sometimes, if I open my eyes slowly, I get a glimpse of one of them watching over me whilst I sleep. Perhaps that's why this bed is special.

When the mornings get lighter, and the days longer, I know that the wet and noisy winters are over, so I want to go upstairs and sleep with my family. I love to spread out across the bottom of the bed and I rest my head on Dad's feet or push against them so his legs fall out of the bed. I am a bit cruel at times as I watch the strange shapes he has to bend himself into just to fit around me on the bed.

Then – it's morning again, and the adventures start once more. I know that I am a very lucky hound and have a relatively privileged life. I am always grateful to those who rescued me and to the family who gave me this wonderful home. Now, where's my lunch?

Dad has taken to mentioning me on Face Book (whatever that is) and I have a number of greyhound friends around the world, including Arthur Carr and Barry Clarke. We often exchange stories via our human interpreters. Due to my lack of teeth and my well-developed tastebuds, I have a varied (and usually soft) diet and Dad often posts what I have had to eat. Now people actually send us e-mails to ask what my menu is that day so Dad or Mam have to report it. Some people believe I live on a diet of smoked salmon and scrambled eggs but that is just nonsense; I only have that once a fortnight.

My memoire came about because at many of the talks Dad gives about greyhounds people want to know about my life story, they want pictures of me, and for me or Dad to sign their book. I wasn't sure at first, but Dad and I talked it over and we decided that rather than just write an updated version of "A Hound in the House" I needed to give my side of the story, in my own words. I thought that this was a terrific idea. This is why I've sat down and dictated these notes for Dad to write for me. It has taken a lot of time, but I think that I'm happy with what he's written and it's pretty much a true reflection of my life so far.

I still look back to those days in the barn in Ireland where I was born, and wonder what happened to my Mum and my brothers and sisters. I did hear about one of my brothers from another litter – Mr D'Arcy who ended up as a rescue in North Wales. I think back, too, to that cold dark field, my weeks of loneliness and hunger, and the kindness of Mr Jones and Twm the cross-eyed sheepdog. I remember all the lovely people and friends I have met over the years, and of those who I love so much and who also love me. They are too many to mention!

I may have my mental demons, my worries and my fears, and the occasional health problem (arthritis, clicky toes and my corns mainly) but I am very happy with my life; I look forward to each new day, whatever adventures it brings, whatever menu I try and whoever I'm going to meet.

Carefully considering my every word...

A TYPICAL
PENELOPE DIGNAM MENU

Breakfast

Scots Porridge Oats with

Shredded Finely Sliced Ham

Luncheon

A Choice of;

Deconstructed Sardine Sandwich

(Tinned Sardines with flaked bread,

water and chopped tomatoes)

Fine Hound Pate

(1/3 Tray of soft dog food with kibble,

a little water, chopped garden tomatoes)

Mid Afternoon Snack

Sizzlers, Biscuits, Cheese or Venison stick

Dinner

Smoked Salmon, Pasta and Peas,

with mayonnaise or crème fraiche

Or

Potatoes, Fish Fingers, Peas

with Salsa a la Pomodorino (Tomato sauce)

(All served with a smatter of kibble)

Supper

Golden Flakes of Corn with warm water,

milk and lightly flaked ham.

Dad and I winning best in show at a GRW event; below, at
Dad's last book launch (Dad, you're throttling me!).

ALSO BY THE AUTHOR

If you enjoyed this book, why not checkout other books by Chris Dignam, titles below, and excerpts on the following pages.

- "A Hound in the House"

- "The Largest Rabbit"

- "The Winter Hare"

For more information about the books, the author or Penny, go to the Crafty Dog Cymru website

www.crafty-dog-cymru.co.uk/crafty-dog-books/

Or e-mail us;

info@crafty-dog-cymru.co.uk

11 - A HOUND IN THE HOUSE

WHY A GREYHOUND?

I had never really been interested in Greyhounds. When I was a kid I had a dog who was my best friend when growing up. After my wife Armelle and I got together we had often "borrowed" family dogs over the years. It was a treat both for us and for them for a few weeks a year – all had been large dogs, Old English sheepdogs, Briards - spoiling them rotten until they went home after their holidays. I suppose you could say that dogs ran in our family (though not "running" dogs!).

Armelle had gone part-time at work and I got a job only 20 minutes from home which meant that a dog would not be left alone all day, so having a dog would be viable. We then began to wonder what breed of dog to have. Old English? Too big, too much maintenance.

Briard – too expensive, and should we really just line a breeder's pocket? Maybe a rescue dog? That would help get a dog out of a pound, and give a poor dog a home. That sounded morally acceptable. Then, "What about a rescued greyhound? They have a horrible life," became the tone of the conversation at home. Like I said, I had never really considered greyhounds.

Someone in work reminded me that a colleague was involved in Greyhound Rescue. Linda – the colleague in question – told me a bit more about it, gave me some contact names and I took it from there. Apparently the Greyhound Rescue group she was involved with took dogs from the South Wales tracks or from Ireland. They had dogs across the area in rented kennels or in "foster" homes. When a dog was taken in they usually went into a kennels but they would need to be assessed as to their temperament, how they behaved, whether they were housetrained, how they got on with people, small dogs or cats. This could best be done by taking the dog into a real home, to spend time with a family and see how they adjust. This is an important part of the adoption process as it gives the adopter a better view of the dog, and helps to match adopter and adoptee.

Prior to our "house visit" there was a panic over

whether to clean the house or to leave it "lived in" (I can't remember what we eventually decided but it was probably to leave the "lived in" look). The couple who came to "vet" us arrived with a surprise visitor; we had our first meeting with a greyhound face to face. His name was Oddjob and he arrived with his owners Pauline and Rob. He was a mostly black dog, tall, thin but muscley – what in an American novel would be termed "rangy". The obvious question was "Why Oddjob?" He was christened this because when he had been in his foster home he had been clean but left a "present" on his first time alone.

My wife as I said before was already sold on the idea of a rescue greyhound; after meeting Oddjob, I too was sold. (OK - Cliché time) - If any dog could be noble, then this dog was. He was quiet, a strong silence with eyes which looked so very sad and deep. As he sat there you could imagine his forbears lying at the feet of ancient kings and lords in castles and palaces. However, his was not such a noble tale; it was a sad story of abuse, neglect but eventual rescue and release.

Some dogs are with their foster parents a short time whilst others never leave; these foster parents, I found out later, had four dogs that arrived, found a niche and never left. Imagine bringing in an emaciated, beaten, frightened bag of bones and then bringing it back to become a settled, more confident bundle of muscles, legs and licky tongue. Once you build that initial bond it is difficult to break it. But what about a dog of our own? We passed the home check - another hurdle over – one step closer to rehoming a dog.

There was much frantic Internet searching for information on coping with a rescued dog and what to expect when you get them home. Websites were scoured, notes taken and a scrapbook compiled. Armed with this and new-found confidence the following Bank Holiday Monday found us ("us" being my wife and I and our young nephew John) arriving late, as usual, skidding into the Greyhound Rescue Show at Pembrey Country Park just as people were starting to leave. Rob and Pauline and Lynda pointed out two prospective dogs. Fortunately for them but not for us, one, a black dog, had been homed that week.

Another dog standing with two children caught my eye. She was tall, taller than most of the other greyhounds we had seen, white and fawn - like a Jack

Russell on stilts and steroids. She was "smiling"
broadly, a yellow bow hung loosely around her neck,
pushed to one side by her head's perpetual swivel to
watch the action all around her. This was that other dog;
her name was Sally but, well, we were warned, she was
a bit boisterous. You could see how excitable she was.

Game for anything by this stage, I took her lead
and we set off across the park. She allowed me to lead
her as if we had been together for years - greyhounds are
usually lead trained and walk well as they are used to
being taken out in groups by the kennel hands at the
track. As the four of us walked I could see that it was
not just me that had fallen for Sally - Armelle was
clearly besotted. What really clinched it was the way
that Sally allowed John to cuddle her, fuss her and to
take her on the lead. Consider that we were all new to
her, there was so much going on around her and John
was squeezing her like a vice. She accepted it all
without a murmur. We walked her back to the cars and
then had a glimpse of that boisterous nature – two loose
dogs were running a few hundred yards away across the
park. Sally's eyes stuck out like organ stops, her ears
were extended like galleons in full sail and her body
tensed like a spring at full stretch. Then she did it - she

yowled a high-pitched tortured yowl and spun around as if trying to screw herself into the turf. I hung onto the lead for dear life but apart from the yowl and pirouette she made no attempt to escape. You can't beat your genes - three thousand years of breeding and track training do not disappear overnight. This "boisterous" outburst I supposed would also account for the dried blood on her cheek where she had become excited earlier in the day and had nipped her tongue! Still alert but calmer, we made our way back to our point of origin where Lynda, Pauline and Rob stood. As we talked I noticed that on Sally's right flank was a brown patch, about the size of an old ten pence piece where there was no skin and bare dark skin. I could not help but wonder what that was so made a mental note to ask when I got a chance.

That evening we talked and talked, discussing whether this dog would be the right one for us, should we wait for another dog...the discussion was endless and we went in circles like the electric hare. There was nothing for it but to have a proper "field test" so Sally came home for one day the following weekend as a trial. She travelled really well in the car, curious for the first few miles, watching the world go by but this soon got boring so she flaked out in the back of the car. At the house she was soooo quiet; polite, well behaved (though not understanding a word of command!) and the day went well, apart that is from a minor accident on the living room carpet and the fact that she came into season on our kitchen floor! But hey, these are the joys and responsibilities of being a dog owner. She was so quiet that we could not believe that this was a boisterous dog – after all, we were used to very big bouncy Briards – if this one was boisterous, the quiet ones must come with a wheelchair and a drip!

We took Sally back to Phillipa, her foster mother, and said that we would really like her to come home with us permanently. The problem was my having to go into Hospital for three days in three weeks time, which meant Phillipa would have to look after Sal for another four weeks. We felt certain that this would not be satisfactory and had begun to resign ourselves to waiting for another dog. It was, after all, a real imposition to ask Phillipa to house and feed her for another three weeks. What a brilliant person – she said that she would look after Sally, no problem, until we were ready.

We can never thank Phillipa enough for her patience, kindness and her very hard work. In fairness she had the hardest time with Sal; Sal was pretty clean but the final housetraining was done by Phillipa, as well as Sal's getting fully used to being in a house day and night. What was revealing about Sally was something Phillipa told us when we collected her for the last time. The window in her kitchen has a Velux roof window. One day Phillipa when went to open the window with the window pole Sally cried out and flew across the room to the furthest corner where she huddled, cowering and shaking. This had been enough to reduce Phillipa to tears and she sat with Sally for ages settling and reassuring her. What was equally distressing was the dog's fear that no matter how kind people were she was still going to be beaten. Sally had a fear of all sticks and umbrellas. Now we understood what the mark was on Sally's side – evidently one of her previous owners had not been anything like as kind as Phillipa. Later our vet confirmed that it was a stab wound.

The week before finally bringing Sal home had been a frantic one of chasing about for dog beds, bowls, and blankets and reading up on greyhounds. Many of the American web sites provide invaluable information on what to expect, what you need to do and generally explaining how the dog views the new house. Expect a pool of wee, for example as the dog will feel insecure in a strange place and may have an accident which may be a way of making the house smell a bit familiar.

One of the recommendations was for a "martingale" collar, a form of nylon webbing choker specially made for sight hounds. Greyhounds and whippets have long necks that taper which makes an ordinary collar useless. With an ordinary collar the dog will see something, you will feel a tug and turn to see a muscley backside and tail disappearing into the distance almost as fast as the cat it is chasing. Likewise, chain chokers can hurt the dog and cut into their necks. As I was later to find out, a greyhound's neck can be very delicate. Most greyhounds wear wide leather collars but as we were to find with Sally, she could not sit comfortably or bend to eat with one on. So, a semi-loose wide banded webbing collar would be better. A lot of shop searching and web searching resulted in us buying a martingale collar from Austin, Texas. It was red, only $8 and arrived within a week.

Another old wives tale bandied about on the web

is that Greyhounds do not moult (or "shed" as the Americans put it). Whilst this may be true in the US where many states have a settled climate all year round – it was not true in South Wales, however. Sally moulted in bucket loads, fine white fur, and a brush would not touch it. The American sites suggested using a grooming mitt, which is a sort of rubber glove covered with blobs. I can thoroughly recommend it - it pulls out the short fur, which can then be shaken off the glove. This proved to be a favourite with the local sparrows who collected the lumps of brushed fur off the lawn to line their nests. It was good to see that we were doing our bit for sustainability and to support the local wildlife! I wonder how thermally efficient greyhound fur is?

(Excerpt from "*A Hound in the House*", Crafty Dog Books Cymru, 2014)

10 - THE LARGEST RABBIT

DOWN THE RABBIT HOLE

Scutter stopped chewing and raised his head as he heard the car's brakes screeching on the road above. As he looked up from his patch of grass he saw a bundle of brown cloth first fly over his head, and then tumble past him, rolling, rolling, all the way down the bank to the ditch at the bottom. The ball stopped with a thump but the car did not - it continued into the other traffic, horns hooting as it went.

"What's that?" Brownie asked.

Scutter shrugged, "Don't know 'til we go and have a look."

The rabbits turned and shuffled quickly through the shaggy grass and scrubby thistles towards where the flying bundle had landed. It was a rough brown string bag tied with a chunk of equally rough coloured rope.

As they approached the bag it lurched suddenly; the two rabbits leapt backwards in surprise.

"Where am I?" the bag asked in a muffled voice.

Scutter and Brownie looked at each other. "Blimey, a talking bag!" Scutter said to his friend.

"You are on the bank beside the big stream." Brownie spoke slowly, as if he had never spoken to a bag before (which he hadn't) and added, "Welcome to our home."

"I'm hungry…" the Bag said.

Brownie nudged Scutter, "You'd better ask it what Bag's eat."

"Mr Bag," (Scutter assumed from the voice that the Bag was a Mr), "What do Bags eat?"

The Bag moved and sat more upright, the knotted string round its neck looking like a tie. "I'm not a bag."

Brownie shook her head and said to her companion, "He looks like a Bag to me."

The Bag wriggled and the tie around the collar

loosened. Seeing the knot coming free, Scutter tugged at it. The Bag shook again and the rope fell off, revealing, as the cloth rolled down, a small head with a small round face and sharp sparkling brown eyes.   He was not much smaller than the rabbits, with deep brown fur covered in faint black stripes, a pair of folded ears and a shiny black button nose.

"What are you?" the button-nose wrinkled as he looked at the Rabbits.

"Rabbits of course," Scutter replied. "What are you?"

Button-nose shrugged. "Don't know. I'm just me."

Brownie and Scutter whispered to each other and then Brownie said, "You must be a Rabbit too. You must be from a different warren." (A warren is what rabbits call their home).

Scutter nodded and so did the new Rabbit, joining in.

"So how did you get in the bag?" Brownie asked, kicking at the pile of cloth with her foot. "That's a really clever trick."

"Dunno," the new rabbit answered.

"Where is your home? Are there other rabbits there like you?"

The new rabbit shrugged, "I don't know where I am so I can't say how far I am from home. I live in a shed in a basket." The new rabbit's face brightened, "-perhaps you know it? It's made of wood and smells of…well…rabbits I guess. And it's blue."

Brownie and Scutter frowned and shook their heads, "There's no sheds like that round here. We're on the edge of the small wood." To be fair, they did not really know what a shed was anyway.

"What about the rest of your family?" Scutter enquired.

Again the new rabbit looked a bit awkward. "There's only me. I had brothers and sisters but they've all gone."

Scutter shook his head. He found this difficult to believe. "What about your mum and dad?"

"I never had a Dad and Mum left us ages ago." As Mr Bag talked he could feel his eyes stinging as tears began to form.

This made Scutter and Brownie feel really uncomfortable, seeing him getting so upset. "Never mind," Scutter said trying to sound bright and buck the little rabbit up a bit, "Come home with us." He put his arm across the new rabbit's shoulder and gave him a hug. Brownie smiled at the sad rabbit too and it made him feel better.

"What's your name; we can't keep calling you Mr Bag as you clearly aren't one," Brownie told him.

"I don't have a name. The people called me lots of things. They said I was rubbish." He paused. "That must be my name."

"Well Rubbish, come home with us and we'll sort out how to get you back to your home."

"Yeah," said Brownie and she too gave Rubbish a hug. "Bluebell will know how to find your home and your family. She knows everything."

Scutter pulled the bag off Rubbish's feet and he

stepped out. They hopped together (well, he did not hop like the other rabbits, his was more a sort of walk) down the embankment, along a winding path through the edge of a patch of woodland to the entrance to the warren, a large rabbit hole under an old and spiky hawthorn tree.

"Come on in," Brownie called over her shoulder as she hopped into the tunnel. Rubbish stopped, feeling a bit frightened. "But it's dark…" he said. He shivered a little; Rubbish did not like the dark. He had spent a lot of time on his own in the dark in the shed and it was something he had never got used to. Scutter stood behind him and he gave him a helping shove. Rubbish reluctantly slid and shuffled down the passageway, the other rabbits encouraging him with kind words and gentle pushes. Brownie led the way, Rubbish followed and Scutter trailed behind. He could not help noticing that Rubbish had a short straight tail, nothing like a scut (a rabbit's fluffy tail). He was definitely a different type of rabbit to the rest of them.

Deep down in the burrow (another name the rabbits use for the tunnels they call home) the rest of the rabbits were either dozing or cleaning out their bedding. Rubbish had expected it to be dark under the ground and smell of damp but it was not; it was really quite light and smelled of rabbits; not a dirty smell but more of a welcoming smell of warmth that seemed to wrap itself around you like a comfy blanket. In the centre of the huddle there stood one rabbit much bigger and browner than the others who they all seemed to listen to without any questions. This was Bluebell, the Mother Rabbit who literally ruled this roost. She was calling out orders to everyone as food was brought from distant tunnels and was allocated, fairly, to everyone there.

"And who do we have here?" She turned to face Brownie and Scutter and Rubbish who stood in between them hoping that he would blend into the background.

Rubbish looked down at his feet and just mumbled something. He could feel the eyes of all the rabbits watching him and he could also feel his cheeks get warm as he began to blush under his brown stripes.

"Speak up, I can't hear you." Bluebell prodded.

Scutter answered for him, "His name's Rubbish and we found him dumped by people."

Brownie nodded emphatically, "In a bag, he was tied up in a bag... it was horrible, Mum".

Scutter continued, ignoring Brownie's interruption, "He doesn't know where his warren is. So I said until he can find it he could come here. He has nowhere else to go."

"Oh, has he not?" Bluebell's voice softened. She lifted Rubbish's chin with her paw and looked into his sad brown eyes. "I'll not have any child abandoned whilst I have food and a roof to give them. Welcome to the warren young Rubbish." She ruffled his chin and Rubbish smiled and gratefully answered with a shy, "Thank you very much."

"You can stay here as long as you need to or until we can find your family and get you home. Rubbish…that's a daft name for a Rabbit," said Bluebell shaking her head and tutting, "And you are the strangest looking rabbit I have ever seen." She looked at the skinny little brown and black stripy bunny. His legs looked very long for a rabbit…and then there was that tail…

"Remember that funny fat one we met with droopy ears," one of the other Rabbits said. This rabbit was dark grey, very big and plump and had a deep gruff voice.

"Yes, Dad," said Scutter nodding. "That was Freddy and he said he was a Belgian Lop or something."

"Belgian, huh! He was only from a few fields away, I could tell by the way he talked," replied Bluebell. "Right then everyone, excitement over! Wash your paws and sit to eat," she called out to the warren.

Rubbish washed his paws with a tongue longer and pinker than any of the other rabbits, then with the rest of the warren sat to eat the food he was so kindly given. It was really nice but not what he was used to - dandelions and carrots and other vegetables. Tasty and crunchy, not like the sloppy boiled up veg he had been given by the people. There the food had been mostly water with a few soft, mushy potatoes and carrots and maybe some green cabbage stalks. The other rabbits all ate away though Rubbish could feel each of them in turn looking at him and he could hear the occasional comment about "Big feet," or "Long nose" or even "Big teeth."

(Excerpt from "***The Largest Rabbit***", Crafty Dog Books Cymru, 2016)

.

10 - THE WINTER HARE

THE LONGEST WINTER

Finn the deerhound was dosing as usual on his chaise longue in the garden. Beside him lay a large bowl of dog biscuits – chocolate flavour (not real chocolate of course as that is bad for dogs), a bowl of water and an empty dog bed. It was empty because its occupant, Rubbish the Rabbit hound, was nowhere to be seen as he had gone off on another adventure. Finn yawned; he liked the occasional adventure, but never before lunch if he could help it. The sun was shining on the garden, reflecting off the grass and the empty flower beds; the plants were growing slowly but it was too early in the year for them to have opened their delicate coloured faces yet. Finn sniffed; winter was a bit slow to finish this year though by the look of Finn's magical garden you would not have known it. With his incredible hearing he could hear a commotion in the distance as something was coming closer and in a very noisy hurry.

He looked up towards the tall door at the far end of the garden, the one that opened onto the meadow and then the deep wood. He could make out a pointy brown nose pushing through and then shoulders and with a "plop!" out sprang Rubbish as he sped down the garden towards Finn. He had a wet puddle on the bridge of his nose.

"Mr Finn! Mr Finn!" he called as he skidded to a halt on the lawn in front of the huge grey shaggy deerhound. "The woods are all white and it's really cold and it makes my feet hurt."

Finn smiled, "What ho, my young pup? Slow down and start again. What are you talking about?"

Again Rubbish babbled, "Really cold stuff, on the ground, in the trees, it's wet," he was panting and puffing with excitement. "I even brought some to show you – look, here on my nose". His eyes crossed as he tried to point out the wet patch on his nose.

Finn laughed, "I fear there's nothing there, Rubbish, just a puddle of water."

Rubbish sighed loudly in disappointment and sat down, "Aw...I really wanted to show you. It must have fallen off my nose."

"Not to worry, my boy. I think it must have melted, which gives me a clue as to what is happening outside the garden." Rubbish looked at the deerhound in awe, mouth open. "I think it must have snowed outside and that's what the white stuff is. Just snow."

Rubbish was even more in awe, "You're so clever Mr Finn." He paused. "But why is the snow outside the garden and not in here?"

"Ah, that, my boy, is because," his brow wrinkled and he leant in closer to Rubbish, " this garden is magic! It cannot snow in here."

The little rabbit hound was now so amazed he thought he would burst. "Cor!" was all he could say. He lay at the deerhound's feet to catch his breath, still a bit upset that the lump of snow had seen fit to melt and disappoint him so much.

Finn chuckled. He thought back about how Rubbish had come to live here in the walled garden. It had all begun when an old cloth bag was thrown from a speeding car. The two rabbits that saw the bag roll down the bank had helped to open it and out popped a little bundle of stripy fur. The stranger was not sure what his name was, but thought it must have been Rubbish as that's what the people had said he was. The rabbits all decided he must be a rabbit too, so they took him home to the burrow where, over the weeks he grew taller, longer and pointier than all the other rabbits. They said he was, "The largest rabbit they had ever seen." He knew he looked and acted differently to the other rabbits but he loved them as his family and they loved him too - he was just a funny looking rabbit.

It was after meeting the mighty Finn, who was after all a very well educated, cheerful old deerhound, that Rubbish realised he was not a rabbit but a dog like Finn. Finn said that he was a greyhound, though he then declared that the pup should be called a rabbit hound as he protected the rabbits. In the "magic" walled garden Rubbish met Finn's owners the Maid and the Butler, and their neighbour Jeffrey, an ancient, balding and even wiser (or so he told them) marmalade cat. Together they had defeated an evil fox and his henchmen (two weasels) who had tried to grab all the rabbits in the warren. Realising that he was getting too big to live with the rabbits, Rubbish was taken in by Finn, the Maid and the Butler but every day Rubbish still visited the rabbits to see that they were safe and do what all good rabbit hounds do. Everyone still agreed though that he was the Largest Rabbit in all the world.

Finn knew that the lack of snow was not really magic, it was just something to do with it being a high walled garden and facing south…or was it west…anyway he'd heard the Butler telling the Maid some time ago. It could snow in here but it very rarely did. However, this long winter was never ending and it was only a matter of time before the snow came inside. Day by day it was creeping closer to the outside of the garden walls. When would it be over and spring come at last? A better question was - why was this winter so very long?

At the same time that Rubbish and Finn were talking, far across the wood two very curious young rabbits, Brownie and Scamp, were looking out of the main doorway of the Warren. Yesterday Scamp and Scutter had been helping their Dad Bob to clear some of the snow away but overnight it had snowed again and they could hardly find their way out towards to the woods. "We'll ask Rubbish to help when he comes over later," Brownie told Scamp. "He's got big strong legs and can dig even faster than us."

Scamp nodded, "Maybe Finn will come too and he's got HUGE feet so can shift even more snow."

"Talking of Huge Feet - what's that?" Brownie could make out some prints in the snow.

"Huge footprints," said Scamp.

Brownie shook her head, "I know that, thicky! But whose footprints?"

They seemed to have come from the hillside away to their right, along the edge of the woods, and then stopped. The prints seemed to have wandered around the Warren entrance, and drifted off back towards the woods.

"Don't know what feet made these," Brownie said.

Scamp looked at his own foot print next to the strange ones, "They are not ours. They're much bigger."

"They do look like rabbit prints though."

Brownie examined the new prints and their own. "But made by a large rabbit."

At that Scamp laughed out loud, "Nah, the largest Rabbit is our Rubbish and they aren't his!"

Brownie whispered to herself, "Then whose prints <u>are</u> they?"

The person who had actually made the prints was standing not too far away in the trees, from where she quietly watched the two rabbits. She was feeling very tired and weak but even so she was also extremely wary. She had lost some blood from a nasty wound but she had stopped it bleeding so that it left no trail now, it just gave her some pain and sapped her strength. If the rabbits had seen her they would have thought she did look like a large rabbit, with bigger ears and a beautiful white coat, except where the red mark in her side above her leg had bled – that part was a deep, dark red. She knew she had to find shelter and food, and then she needed to get home. Winter was here and it was never ending. She sighed and looked up into the deep grey clouded sky - and it would not end until she got home. As she stepped away into the woods she wiped a tear from her cheek and it dropped onto the snow. Where it hit the snow it melted a little gap and almost as quickly a green shoot pushed through and burst open – it was a tiny snowdrop flower.

(Excerpt from "*The Winter Hare*", Crafty Dog Books Cymru, 2018)

For more information about the books, the author or Penny, go to the Crafty Dog Cymru website

www.crafty-dog-cymru.co.uk/crafty-dog-books/

Or e-mail us;

info@crafty-dog-cymru.co.uk

ABOUT THE AUTHOR

Chris Dignam grew up in a happy family home in Swansea, South Wales with his Mam, Dad and a Shetland sheepdog called Shandy. His was a typical Welsh family, though there were (by that generation) no miners and no-one played rugby. Maybe the stereotype failed because his Dad was half Irish. However, they were all short, including the dog.

He is married to Armelle and together they started a Craft business, branched out into Jams and Chutneys and then started Crafty Dog Books Cymru. All this came about by accident after helping with a greyhound rescue charity. When not assisting with the glass-painting or stirring marmalade or acting as Butler to Penny their own rescued Greyhound he tries to find time to write.

His loves are his wife and rescued greyhounds (though he says not necessarily in that order!), and music. And writing. And holidays in the motorhome. Maybe that's his favourite? This is his great dilemma

Printed in Poland
by Amazon Fulfillment
Poland Sp. z o.o., Wrocław